'Tears & Laughter'

The first **21** years of Keech Hospice Care

Consulting Editor: **Mike Keel**

Chief Executive

Keech Hospice Care

Great Bramingham Lane

Streatley

Luton

LU3 3NT

ALTMAN

'Tears & Laughter'

Published for Keech Hospice Care by Altman Publishing
7 Ash Copse, Bricket Wood, St Albans AL2 3YA, UK

www.altmanpublishing.com
info@altman-publishing.com

First published 2012
© Keech Hospice Care
www.keech.org.uk

Cover design: Fourth Monkey Limited. www.fourth-monkey.co.uk
Book design: Fourth Monkey Limited. www.fourth-monkey.co.uk
Printed and bound by Chiltern Printers (Slough) Ltd

British Library Cataloguing in Publication Data

Keech Hospice Care – the first 21 years
M Keel

ISBN 978 1 86036 046 6

Disclaimer

Contents

Index

"With such busy lives,
do any of us look back and take stock of how things have come together
over the years ?"

Preface

"It has been a humbling and amazing journey talking to the many people involved in the charity's history and listening to their stories of how they shaped and grew the organisation. The authors and researchers feel honoured and privileged to have been involved."

With such busy lives, do any of us look back and take stock of how things have come together over the years?

This book offers a unique glimpse into Keech Hospice Care. How, from a germ of an idea back in the eighties, the charity has grown into a place that has touched the hearts and been an inspiration to thousands of people during its first 21 years. We have packed the pages of this book with remarkable stories about people connected to the adult and children's hospices: the member of staff who has been with the charity from day one; the volunteers who selflessly offer their help come rain or shine; the supporter that jumps out of a plane to raise money; the nurses who strive to give the best care at all times; the patient who experiences the peace they need; and the family that finds a way to live with their grief. The reader will find a theme running through the book of 'tears and laughter' but added to this is inspiration, hope, courage, resourcefulness, ingenuity and, of course, love and care. Why did we do it? The idea came from one of the charity's companions during their annual lunch. The diners were discussing how Keech could celebrate its 21st anniversary in 2012, when, as if a light had suddenly come on, Tim Watson suggested:

"Why don't we write a book about the hospice and its history?"

Everyone agreed that recording the charity's history was a great idea and would preserve it for the future. It is apt that this book is about the energy and commitment needed to turn a great idea into reality. Turning this book into reality was not going to be any different. As we researched what would be involved, it became clear very quickly that we would need professional help if we were to do the job justice. As is often the case in these situations, a mix of chance encounters and conversations found us a wonderful benefactor, Lady Dixon, who shared our passion for recording the charity's history. This book would not have happened without her timely generosity.

The Journey

It has taken almost a year to publish 'Tears and Laughter'.It fell to us, as a small team of authors and producers, to coordinate the research, interviews, writing, editing and design work required to get the final 100,000 words and 400 pictures to print. Although we each brought research and writing skills to the project, we had not been involved in anything of this scale before.

It took countless hours of rummaging through old photographs, dusty folders, rusty binders, heaps of official documents and old publications held in the hospice's archives to find material for the book. This was followed up with meetings and interviews with lots of people, who also provided photographs, newspaper cuttings and other memorabilia to be included. The enormity of the project was daunting but never dull!

We couldn't have achieved so much in such a short time were it not for a team of volunteers who gave their time to pour over the archives and memories to piece together the story of the hospice.

This fabulous team of four – Richard Field, John Maddox, Phyllis Edwards and Shirley Noller – had all been members of staff or volunteers at the charity from the early days. Their recollections were invaluable in helping us piece together the story and make sense of the information we had. This created a collage of the 21 years, a 'backbone' for the book. We would like to thank them so much for their help.

We must also give special thanks to Julie Jefferson, who transcribed hours of recorded interviews for us and to Mike Keel, the Chief Executive, for having faith in us and supporting the project so encouragingly.

An extraordinary tale

The enthusiasm with which contributors offered us their stories and memories made the task of organising the material into chapters seem impossible. Alongside this, the lists of 'things to do' and 'people to see' grew. But the energy of everyone involved rubbed off on us and the hard work has been well worth it.

The final result is not just a history; it's a STORY still being told. We feel very proud to be part of it.

'Tears and Laughter' is a testament to the hospice, its work and everyone who has been associated with the charity over its lifetime. It is for this reason that we chose not just to write a description of what happened, when and where, but to sprinkle the pages of this book with the voices of the people who were there at the time. We also decided early on that we would include some features that show some of the more personal moments people have shared with Keech. It's an open-ended creation: it is these tales of people who joined Keech at some point along its journey that made the story.

For this is really what this book is about – ordinary people, facing an inevitable part of life – death and dying. That said, it is also a story of something extraordinary – of all the people who have freely given their care, love and devotion to a stranger; of how one charity has made such a significant connection with its local community; and of how the experiences people have at the end of life have, through Keech, been made into something much better.

We very much hope, in reading through the pages of 'Tears and Laughter', that like us, you will come away feeling a true sense of amazement, wonder and inspiration.

This first and foremost is a tribute to you, the people of the hospice.

Thank you to everyone.

Authors, Aurelija Dugnaite and Catherine Mahmutaj, and producer, Jacqui Shepherd

Acknowledgements

The formidable task of gathering the history of the first 21 years of our hospice was made considerably less difficult by a host of people and a sincere gratitude goes to all who never ceased in helping until the finish line.

This book was made possible by Lady Dixon.

As the hospice itself, the book would have not been possible without Dr Wink and Iris White and the initial trustees of the Luton and South Bedfordshire Hospice.

Generous research assistance was provided by a group of volunteers, John Maddox, Phyllis Edwards, Shirley Noller and Richard Field.

For sharing their memories, knowledge and materials for the book, the authors of this book would like to thank the following people for their contribution:

Ann Bates	Jo McDonnell
Audrey Strudwick	Joan Gray
Barbara Kettley	John and Ellen Every
Bev Creagh	John Quill
Brenda Evans	Kathy Scott
Bruce and Zena Skinner	Lesley Skerman
Carly Swaine	Maria Marshall
Carol Bagni	Marian Townsend
Dennis Keech OBE	Mark West
Dorothy Cullen	Martin Johnson
Dr David Siegler	Mary Wang
Dr Elizabeth Horak	Michael and Peter Henman (T&E Neville)
Hilary Corfan	Pam Rhodes
Geoffrey and Janet Squires	Pat Jefferson
Geoffrey Farr	Roger Sharp
George Pearce	Ruth Hammond
Gill Abbott	Sarah Clark
Jack and Lyn Sapsworth	Tim Watson
Jake Humphrey	

Our deepest *appreciation...*

Our deepest appreciation is extended to the patients and their families, whose stones are featured:

Alice
Andrea Pollard, mum to Rebecca and daughter of Marguerite
Caroline Kelly, Declan's mum
Carolyn Heard, Matthew's mum
Colin Chapman and Tina Dodge
Daphne and David Hill
Daphne Bowers
Jane and Andy, Parents of Emma
Jane Boast, Catherine's daughter
Judith, Charlotte's Mum
Karen Harrison, Cameron's mum
Louise Brazier, James's mum
Margaret Pike
Misti and Matt Brandon, Abbie's parents
Paul and Carolyn Wright, parents of Zoë
Phillip Knight
Sarah Bates
Steve and Pam Long, Lily's parents
Tony Bignell

We also thank local companies and clubs, who wrote contributions:
Chalgrave Manor Golf Club
First Choice
Freemasons of Bedfordshire
Friends of Keech, Bedford
Friends of Keech, Luton and South Beds
Luton Library
Pasque Harmony
South Beds Golf Club
The Luton News and Dunstable Gazette
The Rotary Club of Luton
Vauxhall
The Luton News, Dunstable Gazette and Herald & Post for their kind permission in allowing us to reproduce articles and photographs from their newspapers.

We thank Sir Samuel Whitbread for the foreword.

To all current Keech Hospice Care staff, volunteers and supporters who contributed to the book with their memories, comments and suggestions

To Dr Peter Altman for all his advice and his support and to Fourth Monkey for all their creative input into the design of the book.

Finally, thank you to all who have bought this book

This has been a privilege. Thank you for sharing it with us.

Jacqui, Aurelija & Catherine

Foreword

I have been honoured to play a small part in the first twenty-one years of Keech Hospice Care and I am delighted to contribute a Foreword to this remarkable book.

In 1986 at Dr 'Wink' White's retirement party, his wife Iris was heard to say "…he is not going to retire, he is going to build a hospice." And so, twenty six years later, with the help of countless friends and supporters, South Bedfordshire now has an adult hospice, a children's hospice and a palliative care centre.

The hospice has attracted the attention of Members of the Royal Family over these years. First in 1991, HRH The Duchess of Gloucester opened what was then known as the Luton and South Bedfordshire Hospice. Nine years later in the year 2000, HRH The Princess Royal opened Keech Cottage Children's Hospice named after Dennis Keech who contributed £1 million to the project. Finally in 2005, HRH The Countess of Wessex visited Keech Cottage as part of the hospice's 5th birthday celebrations.

As The Queen's representative (Lord Lieutenant) for Bedfordshire, I have been involved in the planning of these visits and have seen at first hand the care shown by the staff and volunteers and the feeling of ownership they demonstrate. Keech Hospice Care belongs to the local people and that is its greatest single asset.

This book, a record of the first twenty one years of the charity, is a story told by the individuals themselves who not only have brought it successfully to where it is today, but who continue, year after year, to raise the £5 million to keep it going.

The communities in Bedfordshire, Hertfordshire and Milton Keynes are indeed fortunate to have such a dedicated group of nursing staff and volunteers to deliver such a marvellous and much-needed service.

Sir Samuel Whitbread KCVO

Dedication to Keech

...A place of *Love*...

What is Keech?

A building on the outskirts of Luton – no, of course, it's much more than that. A place where very ill people can spend their time – yes, but it's still more than that. A service to the community – yes, true, but that doesn't quite cover it. No, Keech is a place of love, that's what it is.

A place where people of all ages, who are in critical conditions, receive the utmost care and devotion, from complete strangers, without any conditions attached.

A place where loved ones of those who are ill can receive help, support and relief from the emotional and physical demands of caring for someone who is so dependent on them.

A place that recognises you are not a carer, you are a husband, who cares. Keech is a haven of love and devotion to make things easier for those who most need it. And Keech is there when the thing you most dread, happens, and helps you carry on.

Thank you Keech for loving my family and all the families over the last 21 years.

Steve Kay

Chapter One

Inspiration: the start

Dr 'Wink' White

" I'm afraid he's not going to retire,
he's going to build a hospice. "

It started in 1986 when I had to retire. I had been in general practice in this area for some 36 years, based in Barton, and dealing with all the surrounding districts. My eyesight was beginning to fail and I knew my time was up when I visited a patient in Greenfield. My wife shone the lights of the car so I could see my way to the front door. Once inside there was only a dim light bulb on the stairs and in the bedroom. When I got to the bedroom I couldn't find the patient. I felt all over the bed – no patient. In fact she was sitting on an armchair in an alcove by the window. I had to ask her husband to direct my hands to her. I came out and said to my wife: "Look, I think I'm going to have to retire."

At my retirement party in 1986, attended by the local press, my dear wife Iris heard a journalist remarking that her husband was 'rather young to retire'. Without any instigation from me Iris said: "I'm afraid he's not going to retire, he's going to build a hospice." So that's how the hospice began.

Prior to that Iris had been working for seven years as a volunteer nurse at St John's Hospice at Moggerhanger (run by the Sue Ryder organisation). She saw the desperate need for a hospice in this area, especially for the benefit of patients' relatives, who would be able to avoid the long journey by public transport via Bedford. Our great friends John and Ellen Every, fellow members of the congregation at St Margaret's in Streatley, organised a dinner party in June 1986 just before my retirement to discuss our recent holidays in Greece. The after-dinner conversation quickly got round to a hospice. After some discussion John said: "Well, if you're going to start a hospice I will help." And so the idea of the hospice began, with headlines in the paper the next day: 'Doctor to retire, but not to retire – he's going to build a hospice.' Support for the idea came flooding in, not only from the community but also from many, many friends who rallied round.

They were recommended for their experience by other friends. Our first object at this time was to build an appeal committee to begin raising funds and to draw up plans for this new hospice.

Artist's earliest impression of the hospice building.

We recruited influential people in the community who had contacts and skills they could pass on for raising funds and the planning of the building.

One of the first to join us was Ron Upton. Again a fellow member of our congregation at St Margaret's, he was in the publishing world and came with expertise in contacting the media and publicising the hospice, so essential at this time. Next to be recruited was Geoffrey Squires, first treasurer of the appeal committee and later the hospice. He could not have been a better choice. A member of a local firm of accountants, he was cautious in his approach. Geoffrey was wonderful at explaining the financial set-up and requirements to enable us to register as a charity with the Charity Commission.

Around the same time, Tim Watson came on to the appeal committee. He again was so good on the legal side of setting up companies and the legal requirements. Next to be recruited was Geoffrey Farr. Geoffrey was a Luton businessman, a prominent member of one of the Rotary Clubs and very influential in the business world. He came on to the committee mainly to represent the fundraising appeal and later the hospice itself, by promoting it to the business community.

Bruce was the kind of man who, if you needed anything doing at or for the hospice, was your first port of call.

We also had Iris, the instigator of the appeal, who came with her knowledge of nursing. She had been a registered nurse and qualified midwife for many years but her experience as a volunteer at Moggerhanger was essential, not only on the appeal side but also on the planning of the future hospice.

We had dear Betty Robinson, who was against any kind of publicity, but who was the main benefactor of our local hospice. Without Betty we would not have obtained suitable land nor the initial financial wherewithal so vital to achieve our aim. Betty's generous donation, with the support of John Every, who was responsible for introducing us, got the appeal off to a wonderful, wonderful start. John, a teacher, was very knowledgeable on the set-up of various local charities and legal trusts to which we could apply. John eventually became our appeal director.

We also had Roger Wood, the local Vicar at St Margaret's. A true Yorkshireman, he exuded common sense as far as advice and theological matters were concerned, both very important in the setting up of the hospice.

Someone else who came on the committee a little later was Bruce Skinner, a local businessman who had great influence in the local retail trade, especially through his Rotary involvement. Bruce was the kind of man who, if you needed anything doing at or for the hospice, was your first port of call.

is sister, Zena Skinner, joined the appeal committee later on. She had been a well known TV chef in her early life. She helped design the catering side and, I felt, fulfilled her inner person.

David Siegler also joined the appeal committee. He was a chest physician at the Luton and Dunstable Hospital, a welcome expert on the medical care side. When the hospice was completed, he became our first medical director. David did this all completely in an honorary capacity, as did all those on the appeal committee – a wonderful tribute to them all.

We later recruited Gwen Wells who became a dedicated receptionist from the time of opening the hospice. She was a volunteer in the beginning and worked two or three days a week. Later this became a small salaried position, and Gwen was very dedicated and loyal.

Initially, we used to meet in our various homes where we would share responsibility for light catering and looking after the committees. Later we found offices for the appeal committee in Union Street, just off the London Road in Luton. This was organised by dear Bruce who negotiated with the owners to let us have the space free of charge for a year. I am saying this to illustrate the wonderful support we got for the hospice from the word 'Go'.

So the appeal started and the first fundraising occasion was a garden party at my house in Warden Hill, but after that the number of events snowballed. My wife and I, and several other members of the committee, including John and Ellen Every and Ron Upton, attended these little local dos, our fêtes. But it wasn't all fun and games.

After a year or two, we were beginning to struggle to meet our target, originally set at £1-million in 1986 but later upped it significantly as costs were beginning to rise. It would be a five year thing and we would open in 1991 – and we achieved that.

We often floundered in meeting our financial target. It was only after we had to take on salaried staff to cope with the demand that we began to eat into our funds. At one point I went to my letter box and discovered an envelope in it: no address, no acknowledgement needed – a cheque for £100,000. Another time two little girls brought me an envelope containing about £14. It was what they had collected at a treat day.

I remember Iris being rung up by a patient of mine requesting her presence at precisely five to one. It couldn't be a minute later or a minute before – it had to be five to one. Iris went down and was given a parcel 'for your hospice".

(Top) From the word 'Go': Dr White at one of the early fundraising events

(Middle) 'Pegging out': Dr White, Bob Monkhouse and his wife and John Every (centre)

(Bottom) The hospice's first newsletter in The Luton News, February 1989

She then had her hair done in Luton, got stuck in road works and thought 'I'd better see what's in the parcel.' It was stuffed full of notes. I said: "Don't go anywhere, go straight down to Geoffrey Squires and give it to our treasurer." It turned out to be £30,000 in different denominations. We also had legacy donations at a very early stage. The Luton News and the Citizen both adopted the hospice as their charity, so we managed to get pictures and publicity of various events and milestones without any trouble at all. We also got Bob Monkhouse on board, delivered by Ron Upton. Bob came and blocked the pegs to mark the hospice layout and he was absolutely delightful. It was a cold, cold day, but he was wonderful and then came back to our house for a little celebration. I also remember going on the morning programme at Three Counties Radio once or twice to promote the hospice. It was quite frightening. First of all we called the hospice the Luton and South Bedfordshire Hospice. This was simply because Betty Robinson did not want any publicity otherwise we would have called it the Betty Robinson Hospice in her honour for the major support she gave us. But she wouldn't have that so the whole community came to the decision that we should call it the Luton and South Bedfordshire Hospice because this vaguely described the area we were going to serve. But nobody was really happy with this, especially the people of Dunstable. It did cause a little bit of geographic disagreement.

> " Don't go anywhere, go straight down to
>
> *Geoffrey Squires*
>
> and give it to our treasurer. "

As Iris and I were walking one Easter, we came across this little anemone blooming on the hills of Barton Springs. It was the anemone pulsatilla, the Easter lily. We adopted it, with the agreement of the committee, as our logo. I feel now very strongly that it was the nicest, prettiest, self-explanatory logo of the hospice world. There is hardly anything better than seeing that beautiful little bloom support us – a sign

of peace and resurrection at Easter. Many of our supporters were attached to our logo because it was so unusual. It wasn't St Christopher's or St Joseph's – it was ours and it was unique. The planning stages of the hospice required a lot of work and there would always be two of us who would attend the National Hospice Conference in London. It was held under the auspices of Help the Hospices, but it took place at some unusual venues which were always donated to the hospice movement. One, quite naturally, was the Royal College of Physicians, but we once went to a Southern Television studio where we had our meeting in the spectator hall with all the cables and cameras around us. The planning of the hospice had to go ahead with what kind of building we wanted, the policy the hospice would have and the financial support we would be getting from government. Iris and I would arrange to meet fundraisers from already established hospices, and they very freely told us of the difficulties they encountered along the way. To plan to this degree, we visited other hospices before ours was even on the drawing board. We visited Berkhamstead, Garden House Hospice at Letchworth, Willen Hospice in Milton Keynes and the hospice at Windsor, the Rolls Royce of the genre. Each hospice we visited gave us some aspect of design they felt they'd done wrongly that could be improved. So a lot of help came from that kind of source, not only in the planning of the hospice but also in the fundraising. It shows how many ramifications there were to get things for the hospice for as little as possible, and that's how we managed to make our funds go so far.

One of the good things was an appeal for government funding, which was initiated by Stirling Hospice in Scotland. The hospice movement always said: 'We do not want 50 per cent of something, because we always want to be able to be in control.' This was to keep true to hospice philosophy, rather than go into the NHS. The first Health Minister we dealt with was Ken Clark, succeeded by Virginia Bottomley. I wrote letters to both Ministers about how funding should be increased, especially on running costs, not so much on the capital side of things. I remember going to a London Hospice where the Minister was making an appearance.

At that time my sight wasn't very good but she was only going to answer one question so I managed to scramble down a corridor with cables lying about and grab the microphone before anybody else. I said who I was and told her that I was looking for direct support from government towards our running cost and she looked up and said:

"I know you, don't I? I can't answer your question now but I will promise to come and talk to you after the meeting."

Which she did. After this our funding for the running costs of the hospice was set at a total of 42 per cent.

The rare bloom: Pasque flower in spring

This was a wonderful time. Not only was it 42 per cent, but it was ring-fenced for the hospice movement exclusively – not for general palliative care, but just for hospice care. Unfortunately, that was eroded by future governments, when they brought in the customer provider policy. It was up to family practitioner committees to allocate funds to you, and they quite often had other priorities, which as a result meant that 21 years later the funding has dropped to 22 per cent.

I think the hospice movement as a whole must try and initiate a protest and get this funding ring-fenced because it is an integral part of NHS palliative care. Nursing care has deteriorated very badly in our NHS hospitals. And whatever you say and whatever hospital you stay in, there is nothing like hospice care for pain control and nursing care particularly.

After the wonderful support we received from the government and also from the community we upped our target, this time to £1.5 million. We achieved it just as the hospice was being completed, about a year before we officially opened.

Neville's the builders were absolutely wonderful in working around donations that would be given to us by other contributors in the way of paving stones, glazing, windows, plumbing, beds – you name it, we got it. They gave us a contribution too, which cut down our building costs considerably. John Wotton from Huntleigh Healthcare Ltd donated the first beds and medical equipment for the hospice. The hospice build final costs were between £350,000 and £400,000. The first year's running costs were approximately £350,000. That was achieved mostly because, by then, we had a force of 300 volunteers in every area – from laundry, catering and nursing to

bereavement and acupuncture. The hospice was set to open in early 1991 and we started recruiting staff. We appointed our first matron, Barbara Kettley, a Macmillan nurse. She was very, very dedicated to the Macmillan organisation, but also to hospice care. She was absolutely delighted when the committee decided to offer her the job. The standard of nursing, which she engendered in the hospice, was absolutely superb. She advocated holistic care and this ran through the whole of the organisation. People were catered for whether this involved medical needs, bereavement, comforting, liaison with relatives or any other aspect of their lives. We always ran a very open policy. Another was to admit people who had no-one to look after them; whose pain was not being controlled or who were not receiving a good enough standard of nursing care. The hospice would try to arrange to visit them and to admit them as soon as possible, especially when there was a state of emergency. Someone else recruited in the early days was volunteer organiser Faith Tournay, who had established Dunstable's Hospice at Home. Faith stayed for several years in an honorary capacity.

One of the first people we recruited, again as a volunteer, was hospice bursar John Britton. As things evolved, we had to take on more salaried staff including the first salaried General Manager, David Ashton.

From then on, as the hospice cared for more and more local people and expanded in size, service and importance to the local community, the list of people involved started to get longer and longer. I am grateful to see it is still growing to this day.

Hospice contract is signed

PROBABLY the most important event since the Luton and South Beds Hospice project was launched took place on Thursday.

Contracts were signed by the trustees and builders T. and E. Neville for the building of the hospice, which is scheduled to open just before Christmas.

Trustees Dr Wink White, Betty Robinson, Geoffrey Squires and Ron Upton put pen to paper in Neville's boardroom at the Marsh Road, Luton, headquarters.

Dr White, chairman of the hospice committee, said: "This is a momentous occasion for all of us who have been involved with this project from the start.

"It is gratifying to realise that we will achieve our stated target of opening the hospice doors in 1990.

"We are pleased that Neville's are going to build the hospice for us, especially since they are a local company and are also well known and respected locally."

Dr White also announced that all the mayors and district chairmen in

to jointly "turn the first sod" at a special ceremony on the project site at Bramingham on Saturday, March 10, at 3 pm. Members of the public are also invited.

The laying of the foundation stone will be on May 19 and the builders will handover the hospice in the middle of December.

Hospice administrator John Every said: "Although we have the money for, and are actually starting to build, the much-needed hospice for this area, which is exciting for us all, we must not lose sight of the fact that we still need to raise over £800,000 to equip and run the hospice when it is built.

"This year, we need to redouble efforts to achieve target of £1.5 m by December.

Mr Every ap to anyone wh help in any would like the project, hospice Luto

● Signed and sealed . . . left to right, Ron Upton, Mrs Robinson, David Hooker, surveyor; Dr Wink White, Geoffrey Squires, John Every, hospital administrator, Mike Deles, architect; and Michael Henman of Neville's.

> *It's only by a combination of good luck and local knowledge that the initial committee came together from such different, but essential walks of life.*

An idea to build a hospice was to stay only an idea if it was not for the initial handful of people of the original setting up committee. For the bold ambition to take off, it was clear there was a lot to be done: long before the fundraising, the building works and the grand events – all had modest beginnings in the hands and minds of the original hospice trustees.

The first meeting of the founding group was on 14th October 1986. The original setting up committee members were Chairman Wink White, Iris White, John Every, Geoffrey Squires, Tim Watson, Ron Upton, Derek Hewitt and Betty Robinson.

They all were instrumental in their own ways, and it's only by a combination of good luck and local knowledge that the initial committee came together from such different, but essential walks of life: a GP, a palliative care nurse, a teacher, an accountant, a solicitor, an architect and a land owner, united by their passion to build a local hospice.

What fuelled the hospice ambition was their undoubted devotion and a real passion to make the idea work, for which their knowledge, time and efforts were to be committed for years and years to come.

The original hospice committee members in the local news

It all started with £12...

Geoffrey Squires, an accountant, was the first treasurer and with his wife Janet used to attend committee meetings and count up funds at their house. Unaware that the very same bank account will one day see an annual turnover of £2.5 million in just over two decades, Geoffrey was the one trusted by the committee members with the task of opening the charity's first ever bank account in March 1987. Geoffrey was valued for his pragmatic approach to finances, his accountancy expertise and his insightful explanations of how much and when it was needed for the hospice cause to take off. Geoffrey went to a bank in Luton with £12 in his pocket. By the end of April this had been increased to £1,056 as a result of a coffee morning at Dr and Mrs White's house and a local Women's Institute sale.

The Luton and South Bedfordshire Hospice was officially established by Trust Deed on the 7th July 1987. The trustees on the original deed were Wink White, John Every, Betty Robinson, Geoffrey Squires and Ron Upton and the "Trust Fund" was £2,018.09.

The deed was put together by a local solicitor, Tim Watson LLB, who was involved in the hospice since day two. Tim, along with his day job at *Clayton & Co Solicitors*' Luton branch, handled the hospice's legal issues for 16 years and was also secretary to the trustees for several years. He later became the Vice Chairman of the trustees when David Siegler succeeded Wink White as Chairman.

"I knew John Every through his daughter Frances and John suggested to me that I should get involved to help out with legal issues – they wanted a lawyer on board. It was a conscious decision: I had lost my father to cancer in 1973 when I was only 22, which made me realise that a hospital is not a great place to die.

"I remember thinking I wish the hospice was there when my father had died.

"I was extremely sceptical about the hospice ever becoming a reality. I was thinking it's nearly impossible to raise that amount of money – it was £800,000 at the time. I went along with it, but it was very doubtful – it seemed such a lot of money to raise.

"The passion and enthusiasm I used to feel from the others when I came to the Appeal Committee meetings in the Union Street office slowly started to rub off on me."

Fortunately for the cause, Tim had recently completed a charity project, assigned to him by his then Senior Partner, Roy Muller (who was also Betty Robinson's solicitor) at his firm prior to joining the hospice effort, but he still felt it was a case of learning on the job:

"I dealt with hospice matters at night at home most of the time and used to come to Union Street for meetings. Once we got the appeal committee off the ground, we got money coming in, so the first thing for me was to set up the charity legally.

"Roy Muller sadly died in 1986 and David Cheetham (the Diocesan Registrar and Bishop's Legal secretary) became the firm's Senior Partner and also looked after Betty Robinson's legal affairs.

"All my partners at Claytons were very happy that I should work for the charity without any fees; the firm just treated it as our charity. The hospice was our pet charity!

> "The charity was at first set up as a body of trustees with unlimited liability. Once the hospice had been up and running for two or three years it became appropriate to transform it into a limited company (limited by guarantee) which meant more regulation but had significant other advantages.

> "Originally established just to care for cancer patients, I foresaw the need for the charity to look after patients with other terminal and life-limiting illnesses so, when drawing up the constitution of the new company, I included the additional powers to enable it to do so. This is, indeed, how the hospice movement has developed."

Tim remembers St Margaret's Church in Streatley as a 'recruitment hub' for the charity: John Every was a church warden there, Betty Robinson and Iris White were in the church choir and David Siegler, Geoffrey Squires and his wife were regulars of the congregation. Betty Robinson, a local landowner, was involved with charitable work in the local area and supported the cause since she first heard about it. John Every mentioned the hospice idea to Betty at the church, and she at once offered her help with land. The trustees felt that her generous and instant support so early into the appeal gave the cause a real kick start. Tim remembered:

> "'Passionate' is a very good word to describe the atmosphere between the trustees in the early days. Everybody was very dedicated to achieving the target, but there were lots of different opinions as to how they should go ahead and a fair share of heated disagreements along the way. It was quite remarkable that all the right people came together at the right time. It was simply put together, raised and kept alive by friends and friends of friends."

Humble beginnings

Dr David Siegler, a chest physician, first got involved with the cause in 1986 through Wink White. He was a consultant at the Luton and Dunstable Hospital and ran the Chest Department from 1978 until his retirement in 2006. His interest in palliative care stemmed from his close involvement with patients with lung cancer, which was the cause of a quarter of all cancer deaths in the local health district in the 1980s, and was the most common fatal cancer across the whole of the UK. Dr Siegler was instrumental in setting up the medical side of the hospice and remembers much about the early days:

> "Wink and I knew each other because in those days the GPs and the Consultants were very much closer together than they are two decades on. Wink and I are also good friends. He invited me to join the Appeal Committee as a Medical Advisor to the Appeal Committee. I shortly became Wink's Vice Chairman of the Appeal Committee and when the hospice opened I became Honorary Medical Director. I advised on the medical aspects, like the design, function, services and purpose of the build in our old office in 6 Whitehill House in Union Street, our extraordinary little office."

Indeed, if the walls of the Union Street office could talk, there would be tales and tales of very long evening meetings, passionate conversations, quite a few heated debates and that powerful atmosphere of men and women on a mission. From these humble days in the office, the trustees were adamant that as much as possible in the office and community should be done by volunteers in order to save money. One of them, a long serving volunteer Phyllis Edwards, who was also a Director on the Trading Board and a member of the Fundraising Appeals Committee, has been involved with the hospice since the times at the Union Street office:

> "In early 1988 another volunteer Lyn Sapsworth and I joined forces in setting up the Union Street office. We volunteered to support the administration and raise the first funds for the build of the hospice: we got involved in obtaining monies through local groups and businesses. We used to send out flyers, count the monies received and forward 'thank you' letters."

Geoffrey Squires, left, and Dr David Siegler at the hospice's day centre

Phyllis, who has been volunteering at the hospice for over two decades, was introduced to the charity by Jack Sapsworth, Lyn's husband. Jack, a long-term hospice trustee and a member of Rotary Club of Luton, heard about the hospice in 1988 while at a club lunch.

An announcement was made requesting help for the new charity. Jack recruited the hospice's first paid member of staff Penny Westley as secretary. Jack and Lyn would continue their fundraising work for many years to come and to this day.

Getting to know
the local *Comm*

All the early supporters like Phyllis, Lyn, Jack and the trustees agree that setting up the charity in the early days was one of their most memorable highlights during their long involvement. Perhaps, unsurprisingly, the word 'fun' is often repeated by those involved. Dr Siegler agreed:

"The days before the hospice was built were when we had all the fun, because we started from a standing start, there was no money. We started from zero, so the stories about fundraising were quite extraordinary. Early on, it was largely raised from the local community in small amounts, things like coffee mornings. One of us used to go out to meetings and functions. I remember going to a local flower-arranging group. We would give a short talk and then receive a cheque, and that's how the money came in.

"We also had a terrific group of five girls, including my wife, who were the original Friends of the Hospice who used to arrange an annual Charity Ball at New Farm. It was owned and run by Ross Miller. Farmer Ross, who we got to know through St Margaret's, had an enormous barn and, out of the goodness of his heart, every summer he would let us have the use of the facility for free. The girls would put up a marquee inside the barn and that was our major fundraising event. We used to hire a band and we would have dinner. There was one famous year when we had the "year of the hat", where we had an auction which was supervised by Freddy Frost, who was then the Queen's milliner. It really was fun.

"I also remember a time when Wink and I went to the Town Hall to receive a large cheque from a local authority – I can't remember exactly what it was – it might have been £100,000. I think that took us over the million and enabled us to start the building work. I remember then walking arm-in-arm with Wink through the town centre."

The committee had made impressive progress by the end of 1987: charitable status was established; the land was secured; and lots of local support and goodwill was being gathered through fundraising activities, newsletters and local media coverage.

Shaping the services

Apart from having fun, Dr Siegler's main responsibility was to help the trustees shape the new hospice's medical services.

"Ideally, our philosophy was 'people should die at home'. If they can't then the hospice is a very good second-best. That was always our philosophy from the very beginning and is the same today. "People were incredibly supportive because they realised the hospice was going to fulfil a need. There was no way that the hospital was going to be able to do it, simply because of the facilities there; the limited access to beds; and so on. Out here in the country, it couldn't have been better. I think the local community realised and understood it very quickly. Wink was also very well known in north Luton – his practice was in Barton – and it was lovely to see all his patients come up to him. We would go and run a stall somewhere and they would all come up and talk to him."

What has slipped through the memory of the committee has been reliably captured on paper and tucked into a quiet corner of the hospice's archive room. Dusty and weary looking folders hide a wealth of minuted meeting notes, carefully noting what was important and debated in the early meetings in Union Street. For one, the meeting minutes from March 1989 mentioned a list of already 200 addresses of the hospice's voluntary supporters and Iris White reported that 'Friends of the Hospice' group would be hosting their first ever fundraising event, a buffet, on 15th April 1989.

unity

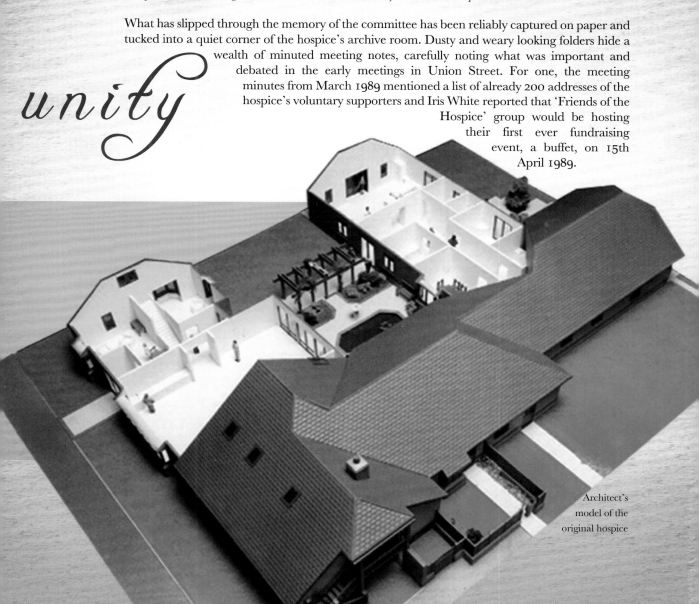

Architect's model of the original hospice

Then and now...

Although the pioneers of the charity have moved on in their personal lives and the hospice has grown under the care of new trustees and staff, the founders still have the place 'in their blood'. For many people who have been involved in the hospice over the years – it never leaves you.

The current Fundraising Director, Jacqui Shepherd, commented:

"Many people will walk in and out of your life, but true friends leave footprints on your heart. The hospice 'family' are all true friends."

John Every resigned in the early 1990s. Betty Robinson continued her support throughout her life and also generously remembered the hospice in her Will in 1999.

Tim Watson was announced a Companion in March 2003 and continued voluntary work until he retired completely in 2004.

"The hospice is undoubtedly one of the most successful local charities in the area. From very early on in the appeal to this day, local people identify with their hospice. They feel it belongs to them: that in essence, is the hospice's biggest success. "

Dr Wink White and the initial trustees have followed the hospice's growth since their retirement and are welcome guests in the hospice at any time. Although the hospice has physically changed dramatically during the 21 years, they all agree that it still bears the ethos of the same place that was thought of during that special after-dinner discussion in 1986. Tim Watson summed up the journey of the hospice from these humble but passionate beginnings:

"It surprises me to this day that the hospice is what it is now: to go from nothing to multi-million pounds worth of services for the community in just over twenty years is quite an achievement to say the least."

"Wink' and Iris's initial idea, in my view, was a cottage hospital – a home away from home for all those who need a sanctuary at the end of their life. The hospice to me embodies that, but also stands for so much more: it has outgrown the original vision.

"Looking back over my whole career in Law, my involvement with the hospice during its first 16 years is the thing of which I am most proud.

"The hospice is undoubtedly one of the most successful local charities in the area. From very early on in the appeal to this day, local people identify with their hospice. They feel it belongs to them: that, in essence, is the hospice's biggest success.

"Now, I must admit I admire how the hospice raises more than £5 million to serve its community every year."

Chapter Three

Betty's land

> " It is almost certain that without these generous donations the hospices might never have happened. "

The name Betty Robinson is synonymous with and inextricably linked to the charity for ever. By donating the land, both for the original building and later for the children's hospice, Betty Robinson provided vital contributions and support to the charity's plans. It is almost certain that without these generous donations the hospices might never have happened.

Betty, a local farmer in Streatley, got to know the initial companions through St Margaret's church, where she was a regular member. Not long after the hospice idea was made public at Dr Wink White's retirement party, John Every started looking for suitable premises. He approached the then Mayor of Luton, Mrs Audrey Bush, but was regrettably told that the local council had nothing suitable available. John discussed the matter with Rev. Roger Wood and then went to see Betty Robinson.

Betty Robinson with a patient at the hospice event

As soon as John Every mentioned the hospice to her (and his search for a piece of land on which to build it), Betty said she would be delighted to donate a lot of land in Sundon. As the legal representative on the committee, Tim Watson became involved in the legal procedures of Betty's land donation:

The committee was delighted with Betty's wish to donate, but as this was discussed in more detail in the meetings, it became apparent that the land in Sundon may not be suitable, due to being too far out from the main centres of population in Bedfordshire. Once Betty heard the reservations, she immediately overruled her agent's suggestion and offered another plot in Streatley, the Great Bramingham Farm, a beautiful listed building on the northern outskirts of Luton.

In 1986, Betty's donation was a definite kickstart to the fledgling cause. Dr Wink remembered:

"Legally, it was a donation and quite straightforward. Betty had a lot of farmland. The land agent who was looking after Betty's interests identified the land in Sundon because it was of least value."

"First of all Betty suggested that we build the hospice at Upper Sundon, as she owned a parcel of land up there. But this was turned down by the committee, because we felt it was too far off the beaten track for people to be able to get there by public transport.

"Without hesitation, she offered us an old farmhouse at Great Bramingham. It was surveyed by another member of our committee, Derek Hewitt, a member of the John Manning Partnership at Streatley. The firm surveyed the old farmhouse for us and said that it was not suitable for converting into a hospice as it would have cost more to convert than to build a new building. So, without hesitation, Betty Robinson said, "You can have as much land as you like to build your hospice next to the old farmhouse"."

It was fortunate that the area is in a unique position for accessibility for patients and their friends and relatives, and also for the future hospice staff. This generous act by Betty silenced the sceptics, who at that time still had doubts of whether the hospice would ever become a reality – it was just what the appeal needed, a real kick start and a new dose of enthusiasm for the supporters. It was suggested the new organisation be called 'The Betty Robinson Hospice' but this was soon changed at Betty's request.

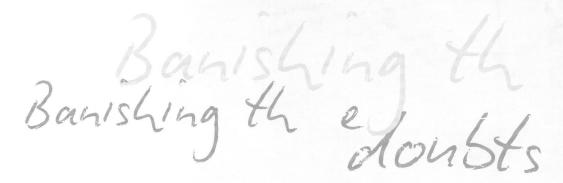

Betty's act of kindness brought a good dose of optimism to the committee members too. Tim Watson remembered how this was the end of his uncertainty that the hospice cause would struggle to take off. Dr David Siegler also remembered:

> " *Without Betty...*
>
> we would never have got started. After we had been given the land it was reckoned then, at commercial rates, it was worth £1 million. Betty gave us that start. "

Elizabeth Horak, one of the hospice's former medical directors, and who cared for Betty at the end of her life recalled:

"She became an example for all of us: not only with her determination to use her assets for the benefit of others, but also with the way she handled the respect and reverence that surrounded her following the significant donations. She was modest, preferred to remain in the background, and preferred not to talk about her role in the foundation of the hospice. Still, she was deeply interested in its development, she found the areas that needed her help, and in her quiet, unassuming way, she was there to help.

"For me, the most important and touching memory was the time when Betty was dying herself. She wanted to stay in her own house; it was clearly important for her. For this, she used an approach that I am sure was her characteristic way throughout her life: she was kind, gentle but determined.

"With this 'Gentle toughness...

She achieved what was firmly in her mind. We offered her a room in the Hospice, but she declined, saying 'I am sure there are many others who need it more than I do'. Although she did not talk about the end of her life, I was sure she knew it was close. She allowed me and some of the nurses to see her at home, and accepted our offer to look after her in her own home. She became gradually weaker, and in the last days she was not able to talk any more. Opening her eyes and a faint smile was all she was capable to offer, but with this, she still maintained the contact.

"It was heart-warming to see this strong lady accepting the inevitable as part of her rich life. She did it with an approach that for me was a special combination of modesty, determination and dignity. With that, she achieved the best in a difficult moment: her last days and hours were spent in a way that was acceptable to her.

"She hoped not to be a burden for anybody, and she accepted her death. Her end, like her life was simple, dignified and arranged on her own terms. She gave a lesson for all of us, not only with her donations, but also with managing her own last days.

Thank you, Betty

Your example, just like your personality, is in the foundations of this hospice."

The homely haven

The design of the building to be erected on the donated land was not only to be functional but also to make the most of the views over the Warden Hills and towards both Sundon and Barton. It was to be, most importantly, a home-from-home that made anyone visiting the hospice feel calm and safe.

Before the donation, the old farm at Great Bramingham was a home to families who worked there. The vast plots of arable land were dotted with cottages and outbuildings, and a gravel road joined Great Bramingham to adjacent Little Bramingham, where Betty Robinson lived. Wendy Ford, a nurse who later worked in the adult hospice, was brought up on and around the farm and remembers Betty from her childhood:

"I was born in a cottage on Little Bramingham Farm. My dad was a farmer on Mrs Robinson's estate and I grew up on Great and Little Bramingham Farms with my two brothers. The farm was full of life: I remember there was a German prisoner of war called Paul, who lived in the farm's converted hen house, who used to tell me and my brother stories. Mrs Robinson was kind to the farmers and thought a lot of my dad Percy – she allowed him to live in the old cottage where I was born rent free until he died. Mrs Robinson's husband died when I was about seven. He was a nice man, but my brothers and I were frightened of him because he used to carry a big gun under his arm to scare the birds when walking in the woods where we played.

'Hospice's angel' dies

THE farmer's wife on whose land much of Luton's Bramingham and Barton Hills housing estates were created has died aged 82.

Betty Robinson, who lived in Great Bramingham Farm until she moved to Sharpenhoe Road, Streatley, more than 15 years ago, came into a fortune when it was decided to build houses on the farm land. She became a benefactor of local good causes, in particular the adult and children's hospice at Great Bramingham Lane.

Described by hospice trustees past and present as "the hospice's angel" and the "grand dame of benefactors", she offered to donate land in Great Bramingham Lane as soon as she heard of plans for a hospice in Luton.

She was a member of the hospice's founding group, which formed in 1986, and served as a hospice trustee up until March 1995.

In 1995 she gave another gift of land for an extension to the adult hospice, providing new day facilities and extra office space.

She donated land again in 1998 for the building of the new Keech Cottage children's hospice and contributed £100,000 towards the hydrotherapy pool.

In addition her charitable foundation has made many large donations for the development and upkeep of the hospice. The adult hospice was named Betty Robinson House in recognition of all she had done.

Dr Wink White, co-founder of the hospice, said: "Betty was a shy, quiet, private person and a shrewd businesswoman. She was difficult to get close to but once achieving that state she was extremely loving and loyal.

"She always put the welfare of our community first which is a tradition I hope the hospice will maintain."

Dr David Siegler, chairman of the trustees, said: "Mrs Robinson, a widow, is survived by her son Mark.

ANGEL: Betty Robinson

BETTY ROBINSON HOUSE

Logo of the Betty Robinson House

"I remember Mrs Robinson would invite me and my brother to the main farm. While dad was busy in the dairy farm, we would sit on Mrs Robinson front porch and eat strawberries and cream that she gave us. It was a busy farm and we helped out a lot as children. Many lovely memories stay with me: while dad was milking the cows, there used to be cats all sat in a row waiting for milk that dribbled on to the floor – my dad always made sure some got on the floor and it was great to see them lapping it up. When I got married, Mrs Robinson kindly gave me the house next door to mum and dad for £5 a week where I stayed until the 1990s. Little did I know that I would come back to the farm to join the hospice years later. Walking up Great Bramingham Lane brought back all the happy times from my past. I felt like I had come home."

In the same way that the Great Bramingham Farm carried Betty's personal touch and homely atmosphere, so too the hospice building reminds visitors of her irreplaceable legacy. Betty continued her support for many years, served as a trustee and was a patron of the hospice too.

The trustees initially offered to name the hospice after Betty, but she refused, preferring complete anonymity. However, the main building is to this day called Betty Robinson House, and the plaque in the main reception reminds everyone of Betty's selfless giving.

Chapter Four

'Hospicitis' sufferers

> " Wink's suspicion that the 'disease'
> was highly infectious definitely was
> beginning to look real. "

Showing their support: one of the many cheque presentations

Dr Wink White showcasing the architect's model of the future hospice

Early fundraising 1998-1990

The hospice appeal's first ever fundraising leaflet

In the second newsletter of the Luton and South Bedfordshire Hospice, Wink White, then the chairman of the Management Committee, remembered one of the supporters describing herself and her colleagues as suffering from "hospicitis". Wink's suspicion that the 'disease' was highly infectious definitely was beginning to look real. With events unfolding rapidly and the land now donated, there was no time to waste. In 1987 the heart of a formal fundraising committee was formed and a list of local people were invited to join. Dr White was assigned the first Chairman of the Fundraising Committee and John Every became the Vice-Chairman. One of the first fundraising events was a coffee morning and bring-and-buy sale at Iris and Wink's home, where they raised several hundred pounds. Support groups were beginning to form in the area and several cheque presentations were made in the very early days.

From these very first coffee mornings onwards, offers of help came from every direction and organisation possible. Local institutes, companies, youth groups, churches, Masonic lodges, Rotary clubs and many individuals and families were coming forward – money arrived from bereaved families in lieu of funeral flowers and people began to discuss possible legacies as well. In 1989 the charity was given office space in Luton and used this to set up an appeals office that became a vibrant fundraising hub. The office co-ordinated all offers of help; stored the goods it was given; and acted as committee rooms for those who were trying to 'control' the dream they had created. Original trustee Ron Upton remembered:

"Things were pretty hectic and a great deal of work was put in by many people, largely unpaid. Gradually things began to fall into place and the outlook seemed very good. We had created a lot of goodwill and many people wanted to help us. We decided to set ourselves a target for building in 1990. Our architect and other members of the committee visited other hospices to pick their brains as we were anxious to avoid too many mistakes. We wanted to create as near perfect a place as possible."

Once the financial target of £1.5 million was announced in the hospice's first ever newsletter in spring of 1989, together with an artist's impression of the proposed building, the feet of those involved seemed not to touch the ground. During the following months the hospice approved the final building plans and several companies were asked to tender for the building contract. T&E Neville won the tender and was appointed as builder. From then on the practical side of the project began to take up a lot of time. Derek Hewitt, the hospice's architect and enthusiastic committee member, took the largest share of this burden and did an enormous amount of work over many months. The building plans were published during the summer of 1989 so everyone could see what they were going to get. By the summer of 1989, the charity had announced that the total income had risen to

£410,000 and gave some details of the ways in which this had been raised: £363,381 from donations and functions; £19,394 from funerals and legacies; and £33,398 from bank interest. The cost of building was planned to reach at least £250,000. Ron Upton, an original trustee of the hospice and one of the first fundraisers, said:

"We were anxious to let people know that we are not spending much of their money on administration. We announced that our total expenses were less than £25,000 including all printing, equipment, stationery and fees."

Fundraising from scratch

Fundraising relied entirely on volunteers' efforts, big and small, as Dorothy Cullen, one of the earliest volunteer fundraisers remembers:

"When I first decided to help raise funds for the hospice in 1986, I used to ask visitors of Luton Regional Sports Centre, where I worked, if they could bring anything we could make money out of. One elderly lady brought in a box full of ribbons and another lady there who did a lot of sewing took interest in it. I sold it for £1. That was the first money I made for the hospice in my 20 years of serving."

Determination and humbleness have been characteristics of the charity's volunteer fundraisers, right from the beginning. In 1987 Geoffrey Farr, a successful Luton businessman involved in engineering and garden centres, was called-in as a fundraiser by the Appeal Committee treasurer at the time. Geoffrey remembers:

"Geoffrey Squires was the treasurer and he raised a few tens of thousands early on before I came in to do the fundraising, because he realised he just couldn't do it. If we only got a few tens of thousands, we would never open. We had to get a good amount of money in."

Geoffrey was not a newcomer to those involved in the initial Appeals Committee. He knew John and Ellen Every, architect Derek Hewitt, as well as Dr

Wink White and Geoffrey Squires in particular. During the crucial first five years of fundraising between 1987 and 1992, the Appeal brought in as many challenges as it gave enjoyment. Geoffrey remembered the start:

> "I went to every business within a 20 mile radius and then I went to every trust that I could think of nationally, like the John Weston charity and the John Laing Trust and others, asking for contributions. My most successful raid was on Vauxhall Motors who gave £100,000 – in four lots of £25,000 each year from 1988 to 1991. That was the first time that Vauxhall had ever done that. That was a tremendous boost, because I was able to go to other firms like SKF Co, Electrolux and Laportes and say: 'Look, Vauxhall have given this. I know you probably can't match it, but how about doing something similar?' Not many people gave on an annual basis, but we got quite a lot of money that way. Still, the great majority was £250 to £400/£500 pounds from smaller firms whose directors were much more involved in the day-to-day community of Luton."

After a flying start among local businesses, Geoffrey's efforts turned to functions. Dame Edna Everidge's appearance at a dinner in Luton Hoo during May 1989 was a definite highlight. There was maximum capacity attendance of around 240 guests and the tickets sold for £60 each including 'champagne reception and first class meal'. Geoffrey remembered:

> "The official launch of our Appeal to raise £1.5 million was held with our great supporters Nicholas and Lucy Phillips at Luton Hoo, who agreed to give the time and the space and everything there. Nicholas went to a function in London and met Dame Edna and asked her: 'How about coming and doing something for me?' She agreed."

Dame Edna in the local news

Dame Edna's signature on the official programme

Nobody realised that Barry Humphries had dinner with the guests in black tie and dinner jacket. He then went backstage and put on his 'frock' before coming back and giving an outstanding cabaret act and doing the auction. The local media covered the event well and the launch got the publicity it deserved and needed. Geoffrey's appeal was officially launched. Back in the late 1980s fundraising wasn't all a smooth ride, according to Geoffrey:

"Geoffrey was very strict about the finances and made it very clear that we had to raise not only enough to build the hospice, but also enough to run it for the first year. Looking back that was such a sensible move because we heard about other hospices opening as soon as they could and then landing in trouble because the running costs hadn't been considered. The main thing in the very early days was to keep the money coming in and keep our head above water."

"Fundraising was very difficult. The costs kept going up all the time, so originally we wanted £1 million and then we wanted £1.2 million and then we finished up getting £1.6 million, which enabled us to build the hospice and gave us a little bit of working capital for the first few months. The hard bit was persuading the people that the hospice was needed. At the time everybody went to the hospital and died in a bed there.

"We had to get the message across that a hospice isn't an awful place that is sad and miserable, but it is somewhere that is happy and where you can get your pain under control and you can actually die with dignity.

"So it was not only the money, it was getting over the whole concept of a hospice."

Zena's brother Bruce, a semi-retired businessman and a childhood friend of Dr 'Wink' White, had been involved with the hospice since the late 1980s too. Having lived in Luton all his life and having run a successful electroplating business, Bruce enjoyed lots of local contacts:

"If they wanted something I knew where to go to get it, or where to ask for it."

The charity's first office in Union Street, Luton, donated by a local businessman John Hudson, was found, free of charge, through Bruce's determination:

"I was working for the owner of the office for a while and was invited to his home for lunch. He asked about the hospice and what I was doing, and I just said: 'I know you've got offices and some of them are vacant. How about letting the hospice committee have one?' He replied: 'Have one with pleasure. You can have it for as long as you want it and there's no charge.'"

Fundraising pioneers

From the very early days, a sister and brother team, Zena and Bruce Skinner, lent their enthusiasm and energy to the appeal. Well-known for her published recipe books and television appearances, Zena said:

Apart from the fundraising, the early days meant a lot of work cropped up on a daily basis and needed a thrifty pair of hands.

> *"In these early days, my role in the hospice was just about anything that wanted doing. I did a bit of do-it-yourself and anything they wanted doing, including help with raising funds, like distributing money boxes. I used to spend at least two or three days a week with the hospice, as jobs cropped up. Once the hospice was built, my usual tasks would involve putting shelving up in the stationery office or hanging the pictures around. I was up there in the hospice so often I was part of the furniture. But I have generally always been on the fundraising side."*

Raising funds from scratch was not an easy task, Bruce remembers. When he first heard about the plans, Bruce had no idea what a hospice was. He soon found that others in the community didn't either. It meant that Bruce's work was about spreading the knowledge as well as bringing in the support.

> *"I think with the number of initial volunteers that came, it showed that people were genuinely interested in the hospice and many of them were quite prepared to support it back then."*

One of the very first things Zena did was to help sell copies of some special poetry books dedicated to the hospice that had been written by her Redbourn neighbour and friend, Audrey Strudwick (now Tingey). Audrey had discovered her talent to write poems while at primary school, but never went into professional writing. Having won several awards as a child for her poetry, Audrey never thought of taking up writing as a career. Audrey's poems have raised funds for the hospice since the late 1980s.

Audrey dedicated her two books – Poems for Everyone and Rhymes for Children – to the Luton and South Bedfordshire Hospice and its future patients. Audrey remembers:

> *"It was the first and last time I published anything. Having written verses for as long as I can remember, it gave me great pleasure to donate the books to such a worthwhile cause. Every penny raised from selling these books goes to the charity."*

Many people had already placed orders for Audrey's books, even before the printers ran off 2,000 copies in the first edition, which were to be sold for £2 each, with all profits going to the hospice appeal.

The books were launched from Zena's hospice stall at Redbourn's annual charity fair in October, 1989. To increase publicity, Zena also had Audrey on her radio chat show, which further increased interest in the poems and the hospice appeal.

Zena said:

> *"She has always hidden her light under a bushel, dismissing her writing as doggerel. But I've been pressing her for a long time to get her stuff published."*

Audrey explained:

> *"I had always considered it a hobby, you see, while I got on with my career with a big store group. I was always invited to read my humorous verse at parties. It went down very well."*

Audrey's books

The copies flew off the shelves of Zena's stall and from the charity's office in Luton. The success prompted Audrey to use her hobby to benefit the charity further and she started charging for the poems:

"I felt I could raise some money for the hospice from each poem I wrote. Colleagues at work would approach me at various occasions: birthdays, weddings, retirement or just whenever they wanted a dedicated verse for someone. I've now done several hundred of them, I'm sure... I write sad, heartfelt poems and funny, tongue-in-cheek ones too. Everybody seemed to know about my hobby – I have been even asked to write a poem by a nurse who cared for me when I was in hospital. The most I raised from a poem was £50. I also used them in my talks too, which always received a warm welcome from the audiences."

With Zena's encouragement, Audrey's two books were re-published in 2004 with another sell out success. Zena and friends sold the poetry books and other items such as tea-towels (embellished with the Pasque flower) on stalls at local village fêtes and via talks she presented as part of her cooking career.

"When I finished my television appearances I decided I'd give talks, make things and raise money for charity. Then the hospice project came along and I lived locally so thought it was a good cause to support. By around 1990, just by selling a few items, we raised £5,000 in the village and wherever I went out to give talks. But I wasn't going to stop there. I noticed there was an empty shop in the village so decided to ask the owners if I could use it to raise money for charity. Luckily, the owner kindly agreed and let me have it for nothing and that's actually how I started the bigger fundraising. After that, whenever a shop came empty I'd be there ready and waiting!"

Zena and friends used the shops they took over as a base to sell various items – mostly household items they made using their needlework and woodwork skills but also goods that had been donated by local people and businesses. They also continued to take stalls at all the local fêtes they could get to.

"When people got to know about it, they'd ring me up and say: "Oh, I've got some stuff, now clear your car out because there is a lot!". Once, I turned up at a neighbour's house to make a collection and after squeezing as much as I could in the car, there were still five big golfing bags! People were very generous. I also once did a cash collection at Harpenden railway station. I hadn't done that sort of thing before but got there about 6.30 in the morning to catch the early birds. I remember thinking to myself that it sometimes pays to look a bit old and weary as I'm sure I only collected so much because people felt sorry for me and thought I was some poor old soul!"

-For Bruce, the biggest landmark of the huge early efforts was running a Charity Golf Day for the hospice, a project that has now been alive for over 20 years and raised many vital funds.

"The start was hard", Bruce remembers. "One of the earliest fundraising events I got involved in was the Charity Golf Day at South Bedfordshire Golf Club. The Golf Club agreed to hold a Golf Day for free each year. So long as someone could run it then it could take place, and of course they asked me and I said "Yes", and I ran it for the first ten years. The Golf Day idea was Jim Hackett's, who was Secretary of the South Beds Golf Club. We used to write to all the secretaries of the golf clubs around Bedfordshire and Hertfordshire. The members of the South Beds Golf Club got their pals to pay on the day and make up a team. We always had a full quota of people and we couldn't take any more. The first year I think we raised about £3,000 and after ten years we got up to £10,000. Then Jack Sapsworth took over from me and he's carried on since. He's just about done ten years."

The Skinners' efforts didn't stop there. Another great memory was the highlight of summer, the hospice's annual summer fête at Barnfield. As great as it was for raising awareness locally, it also brought in support from various businesses. Bruce remembers:

"My wife and I had a pitch at the annual summer fête at Barnfield. We sold fruit which was given to us by Waitrose. Zena organised the donation each year: she went into Waitrose each week and twisted their arm.
People have always been extremely generous."

A lot has changed now in the world of charity, in Bruce's eyes, but the keen support of the local community is something that the hospice enjoys to this day.

"Today there are so many charities in Luton. I think we get more than our fair share, I think we are the most popular. As volunteer fundraisers, we do try and spread the gospel as much as we can. We had these Barnfield events each year, which got people in and they told friends of theirs and then that developed. I think it is probably very hard to get mass expansion in people helping or offering money because of how circumstances are at the moment. 'I feel the support and awareness have been increasing over the years, but we have gone through a very difficult time recently. If we are not careful and keep aiming for gold we could stumble: you can easily spend money, and once you've spent it, it's gone. 'I still feel very passionate about the hospice. As a businessman, I wish it success based on careful planning."

Zena too has continued to raise funds to support the purchase of new equipment for the hospice kitchens as well as many other improvements at the hospice. Still running the occasional stall for Keech today, Zena, Bruce and the villagers of Redbourn have, in over 21 years of fundraising, contributed tens of thousands of pounds to Keech.

"I had decided that when I got to 80 years old or had raised £100,000 I would stop, but then we reached both those targets in the same year! I don't really bother about how much we've raised. Whatever that figure is, I just think, 'well they still need more money, so keep at it, girl.' So, I may have stopped some of the getting up at six to haul out tables at the local village hall, but I haven't stopped fundraising and, as long as I can still get around, that's what I'll be doing! It's a very rewarding thing to see the work you do benefit the hospice."

Looking back on all the years she has been involved with the charity, Zena says her best memory is still the day the adult hospice first opened.

"We had been raising funds since long before the site had been given so to finally see it open was very exciting. We didn't have a big 'do' but everyone was so happy to have come that far. From that very first day, I always thought how well the hospice had been planned. Every bed had a lovely view out of a window and the whole place felt peaceful and happy. Like most organisations, the charity has gone through some rough patches, particularly during difficult financial times, but today it has a wonderful ambience again and that's so important for the patients and their families. It's what encourages them that this is a place where they can be relaxed and comfortable.

66 What I would most like to see for the future is that the hospice continues to do what it is doing. With times as they are, you often wonder how charities keep going but I sincerely hope *Keech* manages it; that in another 21 years it is still here and that the people who need its care continue to get it. 99

Dr Siegler described Bruce and Zena as unsung heroes who are crucial paragons of voluntary support and in whose early footsteps the many hundreds of volunteers followed during the following two decades.

Reaching the
Target...

Early fundraising efforts in the local community

Such successful early fundraising gave the trustees the confidence to start planning the building. During the summer of 1989 all the contractors were appointed and it was planned to start building in March 1990 with the building being handed over in December 1990. Ron Upton remembered:

"This was a great act of faith on our part as we only had a little over half the £800,000 we estimated we would need just to build and equip the hospice, let alone the final target total of £1.5 million. We were sure, however, that the local population would not let us down, and we were not disappointed."

In November 1989 Bob Monkhouse came to Great Bramingham with his wife Jackie on a bitterly cold day to formally mark out the site. This was intended as the final publicity boost the charity needed to reach the target and, with other events, it did the trick. By the time building started, the raised funds were enough to pay the builders, and by the time the hospice opened, it reached the revised target of £1.6 million. Dr Siegler remembered:

"The very first thing you do is mark out boundaries of the land with poles and tapes and the official title for this is a 'pegging out ceremony'. This was done by Bob Monkhouse and he said to me as we walked around, 'I don't want to say this in public but it seems to me inappropriate that a ceremony for setting up the hospice for the dying should be called pegging out.' He was brilliant. He lived just the other side of Leighton Buzzard and we went to Wink's for tea and cake afterwards. Again, he did it for nothing and told some very, very funny jokes. What a happy memory. The pegging out was done with tape, which we had either borrowed or stolen from the Gas Board or the Electricity Board."

In March 1990 there was another publicity event 'on site', when all the Mayors and Council Chairmen from the catchment area were invited to 'turn the first sod', definitely an overcoat and wellies job! Thereafter the building commenced and people could at last see some really tangible results of the many months of work.

For Geoffrey, once the hospice officially opened it was very nice to see people in the hospice and working – it made it all worthwhile. Geoffrey explained how he approached fundraising with local businesses:

"Businesses generally are not very well organised in giving – especially small businesses that might not have a dedicated department that deals with it. Of course there are exceptions but mostly it's very difficult. I have found the best way to do it is to visit them and persuade them. You can write them letters as an introduction, but businesses get hundreds of applications for money and yours might get lost. Businesses, in my experience, also want to get something out of making their donation.

"I knew people in business, so I knew the managing directors of SKF Co and Electrolux, and rang them up and said, 'Look, I'm on the prowl. I want some money, who do I talk to?' And they said, 'Well, either come and see me or I'll give you a name and come in and see them.' I never keep a record of how many hours I spent doing this. If I have to guess, it was probably three or four thousand hours."

All these hours paid off. After the hospice opened Geoffrey Farr volunteered as a head gardener for about two years, and did all the mowing of the grass and planting of the trees and hedges with a small team of volunteers. As a keen gardener, Geoffrey designed the planting layout of the trees in the hospice's gardens. Apart from these duties, Geoffrey holds other personal memories of the hospice:

"I used to come in to the hospice to see one of the patients, my friend Derek, quite regularly and there was this beaming smile every time I came in, and I used to feel really quite humble. Then there were four-bedroom wards with a single bathroom. Two of my friends died in the hospice and they loved the four-bed rooms because they could talk to other people. In those early days, I don't think anybody really thought that a children's hospice was relevant. In other words, people didn't really think too seriously about the number of children that would get cancer at a very young age and suffer.

Dr Wink White with another 'hospicitis' sufferer: collecting a cheque at Neville Sports and Social Club in 1988

"I think it was as a result of hospices opening all around the country and people realising how well they were doing and how they were helping families cope with distress, that it became apparent children in our area might need help too. This resulted in the children's hospice and the tremendous donation by Dennis Keech. The hospice has also been influenced by changes in government policy and legislation which has changed the way care should be given, in other words you have got to have en-suite.

"I wish the hospice all the luck in the world. It needs it, I just wish that the National Health Service would fully recognise the worth of hospices and give it 50% funding, because I think that is what is needed and reduce the stress on hospitals and the way that they treat old people. I feel that with the NHS, if you are over 70, it looks upon you as being past it and that you don't deserve the care that the younger people get. That's reflected if you go into the old people's wards in the hospital; it is a very sad sight."

Similar ideas, reflecting the opinion of many in the community, were echoed along the way in every function, event and meeting in the early 1990s. The committee and fundraisers used every opportunity to express their endless gratitude to the community, who, according to Dr Wink White, have taken the hospice so much to their hearts.

Dr Wink said...

" You are indeed suffering from that highly infectious, well respected disease, so aptly described by one of our supporters as hospicitis. I am glad to tell you that it is *incurable.* "

A fortunate *accident*

A personal recollection from *Lady* Dixon

There are some supporters of Keech Hospice Care who seem to have fallen into the path of the charity completely by accident. For Lady Dixon, it all started with a bus, moved on to involve a golf buggy and has come around all the way to the present day with the production of this book.

Brief encounters

Lady Dixon's husband, Sir Ian Dixon was Chairman of the building company Willmott Dixon and from June 1989 to June 1990 he took the role of President of the Chartered Institute of Building.

As part of an initiative to encourage young people to enter the field of construction, Sir Ian and Lady Dixon travelled around the country with a bus that had been especially adapted to provide an insight into building work, The bus was fitted out so that youngsters could watch videos about construction, visit real sites and learn more about the craftsmanship involved in the various building trades.

In the spring of 1990, while the adult hospice was still under construction, Lady Dixon who now lives in North Hertfordshire, remembers her first encounter with the charity:

"We brought the bus, along with a group of local children from Robert Bloomfield Middle School, to the hospice so that they could see a building site for themselves. We were doing this across the country, but because we were close to home, I remember we brought my mother along for the visit. That was my first involvement with the hospice and, at the time...

Building Matters bus and children

66 ...I never imagined how much the charity would come to mean to me in the future. 99

A golf buggy
leads the way

It was to be some thirteen years before Lady Dixon next made contact with the hospice. Sadly, Sir Ian Dixon died in 2001 and about three years later, while in the process of moving house, Lady Dixon decided to donate a golf buggy he had owned to Keech. She explained:

"It may sound silly but the golf buggy was special to me. My husband had bought it with some money his mother had left him and during his illness he used it to go around our gardens, cutting bits off trees and enjoying the countryside and wildlife. I didn't want to sell it but wanted to find it a good home. Our former doctor, Rysz Bietzk, thought it would be ideal for use at the hospice where he was by then working and so arranged for it to be delivered there. When I finally moved house, I decided to donate some other things and then somehow got more and more involved over the years that followed – all because of a golf buggy!"

Since that time, Lady Dixon, who is now in her 70s, has supported Keech whenever she can, through generous donations towards building projects at the hospice, through social fundraising and now, by commissioning this book. Looking back, she describes her journey from 'bus' to 'buggy' to 'benefactor' as a mystery even to herself!

"I really don't know what it was that made me get so caught up! I didn't have any personal connection with anyone who had been at the hospice but think the children's hospice had only been open a couple of years and I had probably seen quite a lot about it in the local news...

... Once I did get more involved, I learnt so much more about palliative care across both hospices and I consider myself lucky that I have been in a position where I can do something to help.

When asked what stands out in her mind from her visits to the hospice, Lady Dixon recalls various times such as the opening of the new adult in-patient unit and the 'Walk of Life' pathway in 2009 and the re-opening of the newly refurbished day hospice in 2011. But she's very clear that it's not really the big openings which make the hospice what it is, instead describing its life-blood as being in all the people there, those who work on the front-line and behind the scenes:

"I always see such enthusiasm and compassion from everyone when I come to the hospice, from the nurses and carers to the fundraisers and caterers who make such delicious cakes! There's also so many essential jobs that I come across, like the volunteers who help on reception. These are often people around my age and some have been giving up their spare time for 20 years! Then there are people who help with the laundry, just sitting putting the bedding through the machines. I spoke to a lady there recently and when I went to say goodbye she just didn't hear me. It seemed she was totally engrossed in what she was doing."

" Seeing the difference it all makes to the patients is just incredible too. I'm amazed to see how much work is done actually outside of the hospice, in people's homes and also how the charity strives to ensure every little detail is covered to provide the best care. For instance, adults who go along for day care can now enjoy a range of therapies, even taking a bath in comfort and with the support they need. It's the sort of thing we take for granted but what a difference that can make to a patient's life. That's what makes Keech so special."

21 years – the book and the *future*

Having seen so much of the hospice's work and the people who make it happen, Lady Dixon was involved early on when the charity began to discuss the ways in which its 21st birthday could be celebrated and commemorated. When the idea of this book arose, she kindly offered to commission the work, relieving fundraisers from the added burden of trying to raise the funds needed to bring it to print.

Summing up her hopes for the future of the charity and for this book, Lady Dixon commented:

"While there have been lots of improvements made at the hospices in recent years, it's a bit like your home. There's always something that still needs doing! My biggest wish for the charity is that it always has the support of the community around it. Without the huge band of helpers who get involved, it just wouldn't work. I hope that as time moves on, the next generation take up the cause and see the hospice through to its future.

"As for the book, I'm so pleased to have been able to help with this. I think that anyone who has had some involvement with the hospice will find it interesting along with others with a curiosity about local history. Of course I also hope it sells lots of copies and makes more money for the charity!"

Chapter Five

A dream come true

Acrial view of luton and South Bedfordshire Hospice in 1990

"They say one must start as one means to go on. That surely was the case with the special day of the hospice handover on 14th December 1990."

The dawn of the new decade brought along three key landmarks for the hospice. The first key event was handover of the building at the end of 1990, which paved the way for the long-awaited patient admissions at Easter time in 1991. After the successful first summer, the Royal opening by the Duchess of Gloucester rounded up the devoted efforts of the supporters and set the scene for the hospice's future successes.

Finished hospice building in winter 1991

They say one must start as one means to go on. That surely was the case with the special day of the hospice handover on 14th December 1990, which came not a moment too soon. In front of a crowd of supporters brimming with anticipation, mayors and civic dignitaries from all over South Bedfordshire, a giant pair of scissors was used to symbolically snip a ribbon and hand over the new Luton and South Bedfordshire Hospice on that important Friday. It marked another cleared hurdle in the giant undertaking to provide and run a specialist medical centre for the terminally ill: the Bramingham building was in place, right on schedule, thanks to the army of trusty fundraisers, a dedicated appeal team and the good work of local contractors. Centre stage at the hospice handover was Chairman of the group Dr Wink White, who was praised for his role in turning the dream into a reality. However, Dr Wink was always the first to say that the hospice was not just about one person or a group of people – it had been created by the whole community, which, during these first crucial years, realised the need for a hospice in the area and backed the scheme in every way imaginable.

Half the battle won?

When Dr White retired early from general practice in 1986 he and Iris were waiting for this glorious day until the vision, backed and nurtured by so many like minded dedicated people, became a reality. Conceived during a dinner with John Every, the germ of the idea became an ambition that now was a real brand new hospice for Luton and South Bedfordshire. On the occasion of the opening, Dr Wink White said:

> "With the help of our generous community the dream came true in April 1991 when the new hospice admitted its first patients. We are blessed with a superb building on a wonderful site with loving, caring staff backed up by the largest and most dedicated band of volunteers of any similar Hospice in Great Britain."

The contractors T & E Neville Limited commenced work on 5th March 1990 and the building was handed over on time in December 1990, only several months until the building was set to be opened to the public. Michael Henman, former Managing Director of T & E Neville Ltd, recalled the discussions with Dr Wink White and the hospice's architect Derek Hewitt and others on the Fundraising Committee which led to the contract to entrust the firm with the building. The contract was signed on 8th February 1990. During the building contract Michael remembered the opportunity it gave for the introduction of building skills to schoolchildren and the Chartered Institute of Building publicity campaign 'Building Matters'. The organisers of the campaign brought their fitted out campaign bus with a party of schoolchildren specially to the site to be shown around and enjoy a bricklaying experience. The contract was arranged to provide the hospice with the benefits from savings that were achieved by "in kind" offers from benefactors for materials or equipment and many staff from Neville's were involved in assisting in the local fundraising projects.

The finished building was horseshoe shaped with the middle of the horseshoe being the beautiful south facing patio. To maintain a domestic scale and to set the building low in the landscape, it was mainly single storey, with the office and administration space provided within the roof space. The south-east corner housed the entrance and reception area, and the Chapel/Quiet room, one very important place for the future staff and many of the patients, was tucked just behind them. Dr David Siegler remembers how the Quiet room has carried a special meaning to staff, volunteers and patients to this day:

"Dr John Kneebone, a GP from South Bedfordshire, designed the stained glass in the Quiet room. He designed and made the stained glass, featuring the Pasque logo, as his gift to the hospice, which helped the ambience of the Quiet Room. It was for relatives, patients, or even staff to go and be on their own. It hasn't changed since then: you felt that, in a sense, you were in a spiritual space. It was where Barbara and I used to go if we needed to get away from everybody else and it was respected by everybody. If you looked through the little window in the door and saw somebody in there, you went away."

Dr White remembers how the olive wood cross in the quiet room was brought to the hospice by his wife, Iris. During her visit to Jerusalem, the cross had been blessed in the River Jordan before it came to its place at the hospice. The double doors opposite the Quiet room lead into the Day Centre and the adjoining dining room; through the next double doors were the kitchens, larders, boiler and storage rooms. The hallway, through bathrooms and therapy room, led to the garden lounge, the 'sun trap' of the building, a popular spot for many patients. More storage and the Pasque room were behind the garden lounge. Through the next doors at the far end of the garden, was the 'sharp end' of the hospice where nursing is done: the nurses' station, the medical store, the Mechanaid's bathroom, the Doctor's office, the Macmillan Nurses' office and the patients' rooms. The Heather room and the Lavender were four bedded and the Lilac and Iris rooms were singles. The hallway in this part of the building was connected by a rose pergola walkway across the patio garden. The administration office was in the only two-storey part of the building over the reception/dining/kitchen area.

The Quiet room

In the design, to keep the building as homely as possible, the architects chose soft red bricks with darker brick feature bands. The brickwork has been carried on inside the building, immediately inside the front entrance doors, and also in the internal sitting area adjacent to the garden courtyard. The roofs were covered with dark red tiles and a lot of the windows had dark timber frames which have been stained dark brown and were all double glazed. The building was designed around the south facing courtyard garden, where the visitors and patients would be able to sit outside weather permitting. There were also extensive paved areas outside the bedrooms on the south and west sides of the building.

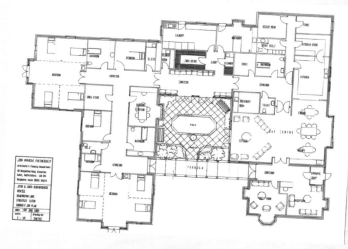

The plan of the hospice building in 1991

Hospice opens its doors

By YVETTE PAGE

A NEW £1 million hospice opened its doors for the first time this week but its future depends on the help of the public.

The Luton and South Beds Hospice held its first open day on Monday and it plans to welcome its first patients in early April.

There is room for 10 in-patients and 15 day-care patients but the expensive equipment will be wasted if there are not enough volunteers to help run it.

Matron Barbara Kettley told the Herald & Post: "We cannot survive without volunteers.

"We need nursing staff, both qualified and unqualified, and anyone else who can help."

A small team of helpers has already evolved but around 200 are needed if the hospice is to operate effectively.

All kinds of help is needed, from driving day-care patients to and from the hospice, to gardening, cleaning, and helping generally with the patients and their families.

There is also a need for people with skills such as art, pottery, or needlework, which can be taught in the day-care centre.

A full-time volunteers organiser will co-ordinate the offers of help and make sure skills are used in the best way possible.

"We cannot survive without volunteer help," said Mrs Kettley. "It is crucial to the kind of care we want to give."

She added: "We desparately need nursing volunteers, even if it is just to sit with the patients and their families."

Open days will be held at the hospice every day until February 17, from 10am to 6pm.

Anyone who would like to help but cannot get to an open day can call the hospice on 492339.

● Matron Barbara Kettley . . . pictured at the hospice.

In the local news: Matron Barbara Kettley shares excitement over the hospice opening

Brimming with *anticipation*

The hospice was finally ready in spring 1991 to show off to the public. A series of open days were arranged for the community in March to come around and see for themselves what they had achieved. Original volunteer Phyllis Edwards remembered:

> "The local community was very generous. To thank them, prior to any patients being admitted to the hospice, several open days were held for the supporters to attend and it was during this time that the public came to realise that the hospice was not a place where you went to die."

What an anticipated treat it was to all those who played a part in putting their hospice on the map, as a long term supporter Brenda Evans from MS Society's Luton and Dunstable branch, who was one of the first to visit the newly built hospice before it opened, remembered:

> "Our Society received an invitation from the hospice trustees to be shown around the new building. My husband and I came along with two other committee members and we were greatly impressed by all the wonderful new innovations and equipment. So much care had been paid to every detail of décor, comfort andfurnishingsand there was a real atmosphere of peace. The enthusiasm and dedication of everyone involved was, and still is truly remarkable."

"The enthusiasm and dedication of everyone involved was, and still is truly

remarkable"

The impression was one to last. Brenda still continues supporting the hospice, as do Rita and Mike Jarman, who first got involved in 1991:

"Our first contact with the hospice was when my mother died in March 1991 just before the hospice opened. After her funeral all the flowers were left at the crematorium, and when we approached the hospice and spoke to the Matron asking if they would like them, she was delighted as she said there wasn't a single daffodil to decorate the place. Since then any flowers left after a family funeral are always taken to the hospice."

Each of the open days that spring served as an opportunity to recruit the vital volunteers needed.

More than 20 of the hundreds of original volunteers recruited during these opening days have stayed on with the hospice for 20 years since the opening, working in administration, fundraising, care and retail. One of them, Mary Moatt was one of the many, who came on board after hearing the new hospice's urgent public plea for manpower:

"My first impression on the open day was one of a very welcoming and comfortable home away from home, ready and finished for those who need it. The tour around the new hospice, made me remember both my parents that I'd lost to cancer and how pleased they would be to see a place like that. I was so impressed I signed up on the spot and marked driving as my preferred volunteering option. I have been driving the hospice patients for 20 years."

Another volunteer Kathy Scott, a long term receptionist, who also signed up on one of the early open days, remembers her start in 1991:

"I was one of the first reception volunteers and I used to go up every Saturday morning from 10am until 1pm - we used to call ourselves the 'Saturday Girls'."

The hospice's list of volunteers was growing all the while. In the end of the first year there were 267 active volunteers: 49 nurses, 52 receptionist-clerks, 17 day care, 37 drivers, 28 meal preparers, 18 laundry, 17 housekeepers, 13 gardeners, 34 flower arrangers, a hairdresser and a beautician.

There was still a shortage of nurses, laundry people and gardeners.

First patients for the new hospice

As is common with fledgling charities, the founding committee oversaw the day-to-day management of the charity until such point when it is too much for this small band of dedicated volunteers. The hospice was no different and it was decided the trustees would take a governance lead, a sub-committee of trustees, fund-raisers, hospice staff (both paid and honorary) and local people from all walks of life would form a Management Committee.

Reporting to them was the House Committee which consisted of the Honorary Medical Director, the Matron and the Honorary Bursar.

At this time, fundraising was kept separate, both in terms of management structure and location. It wasn't felt appropriate for the hustle and bustle of a busy appeals office to be situated in the peace and quiet of a hospice. A separate committee was overseeing the fundraising.

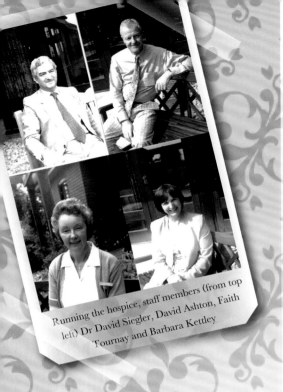

Running the hospice, staff members (from top left) Dr David Siegler, David Ashton, Faith Tournay and Barbara Kettley

R on Upton, a Trustee and the charity's Press Officer at the time, remarked:

"This worked quite well while we were 'finding our feet' but the Trustees later appointed a General Manager for the whole project. Over 200 applicants for the post were received, most of a high calibre, eight were interviewed in January and we were pleased to appoint David Ashton, a very experienced Hospice Manager from Hastings who started work with us on 6 April. He had overall charge of all sections except the actual medical and nursing care which remained under the auspices of the Medical Director and Matron."

The trustees were pleased to see Barbara Kettley, the first Macmillan Nurse in Luton some years before, appointed as a Matron in November 1990. In early 1990 more staff were interviewed and by Easter 1991 all staff were in place and there were 'dummy runs' to make sure everything would run well. The hospice was ready. After the series of open days the hospice welcomed its first patient on the first Wednesday after Easter, 3rd April 1991. Catering Manager, Liz Bradley, who is now the hospice's longest serving employee, remembered the special day:

"We had our first patient come in that day in the afternoon, and that person didn't even make the first night – sadly they passed away. After that we had more patients come in and it started to fill up. But it was very, very different in those days; the patient to catering contact was very much different to what it is now. We used to actually go down to the patients in the afternoon and ask them what they wanted for their tea, their lunch and their breakfast. It was very much one-to-one and you got very attached to some of the patients."

Perhaps, the sad fact that the hospice's first ever patient died the same night he was admitted reflected and confirmed that the hospice was needed for many people and already too many had never had a chance to experience it. In fact, the number of patients admitted to each bed in the first year was above the suggested average for a ten bed voluntary hospice, which confirmed the need for a local hospice.

"I am sure that we *Learn Something* from caring for every individual patient..."

Soon after opening...

Soon after opening the in-patient workload rapidly increased: 148 in-patients were admitted in the first year, several on more than one occasion, making a total of 191 admissions. From the hospice's first 148 patients lung cancer accounted for 27 and breast cancer for 25. Each type for cancer produces its own problems in palliative care and the medical team were committed to building up experience and expertise in all areas. Over the first year, the hospice's occupancy had increased gradually to around 65 per cent at most times. All 10 beds were occupied on a couple of occasions for short periods. The aim was to have at least one bed available at any time for emergency admission, and this seemed to be working well. Ron Upton said in 1992:

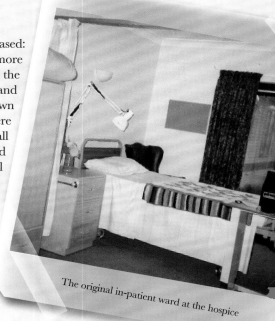

The original in-patient ward at the hospice

> *"Our original estimate of 10 beds being the optimum seems about right, but the hospice is designed so that another four-bedded room could be added with little or no disruption if we felt this to be necessary in future."*

Day care was offered Monday to Thursday, which was more opening hours for a hospice's Day Care unit than usual, and had an average of five patients welcomed per day during its first months. Hon. Medical Director David Siegler said:

"I am sure that we learn something from caring for every individual patient."

Although the original Appeal was for a hospice for treating patients with advanced cancer, the hospice belonged to the UK hospice movement as a whole. It was admitting patients with Motor Neurone Disease for respite care and several were attending the Day Centre regularly. Soon after opening, the hospice was also ready to admit patients with AIDS-associated cancer and complications of AIDS.

By the time the hospice was up and running, Dr Siegler remembers:

> *"Although we were first set up as a cancer charity, we decided early on that we would not limit ourselves to cancer. I think that was an important decision that we would take patients with AIDS and so we had ones who died here and ones who came in to be patched up and then went home. Our respite care was very good. We patched people up and then got them home again. Patients got a great deal out of it."*

People of the *Hospice*

Nurses Sue, Lynn, Elaine and Jeanette at the nurses' station in 1991

The day-to-day running of the hospice rested with the House Committee of Medical Director David Siegler, Matron Barbara Kettley, General Manager David Ashton and Voluntary Services Organiser Faith Tournay. The hospice had no resident medical staff; all medical cover was provided by four local GPs: Drs Miriam Barker, Paddy O'Donnell, Hugh Swallow, Tony Verghese and Hon. Medical Director David Siegler. Each of the GPs visited the hospice for a period in the middle of the day on a set day from Monday to Thursday to admit new in-patients and to deal with any medical issues among the other in-patients. A 24-hour 'on-call' duty rota was shared by all five doctors. David Siegler recalled his sense of achievement:

"We have learned much from our first year, but above all we have remembered the lesson that good symptom control depends on close attention to detail, accurate diagnosis and familiarity with a small number of drugs which we prescribe regularly.

"We have evolved a prescribing policy from which we virtually never diverge."

Recruitment for nurses started in January 1991. Matron described the nursing positions at the new hospice as challenging but rewarding to the 160 people, who attended the recruitment opening days on 10th and 11th January held for all nurses interested in working at the hospice. There were 15 full-time equivalent positions at the hospice, with a majority of jobs being part-time, divided into morning, afternoon and night shifts. Once again the public responded well to the hospice needs: the response was overwhelming, leaving Barbara and the team delighted with the volume of applications. Shortlists were to be drawn and candidates were to be invited for their panel interviews, to join the hospice workforce in time for the two week induction in March. Marian Townsend and Ruth Hammond were among the original nurses, recruited to a job-share position from one of the open days in January 1991. They remembered the interview day:

"The interview day came with snow covering the then tiny lane, creating a great challenge to us, two nervous interviewees. We were interviewed separately by a panel of three – Barbara Kettley, Jackie Tritton, a community nurse, and Iris White. The only question one of us can remember being asked was what 'vices' we thought we had – I'm not telling you the answer! Our idea of the job share was innovative at the time and seemed to be well received by the panel. We got the job!"

Aside from recruiting nurses, Barbara Kettley was set to establish the standards for nursing care, which, in the eyes of many, ascertained the reputation of the new hospice. For Dr Siegler, the reputation then had less to do with fundraising or anything else, it was primarily to do with the excellent care and Barbara's very good team of nurses.

Barbara had been a Macmillan Nurse and done a lot of district nursing in palliative care. Among her professionalism, a light-hearted memory of Barbara has stayed with Dr Siegler for all these years:

'Tears & laughter abound'

In just over one and a half years, the hospice welcomed about 200 patients into the in-patient unit and at least 50 into Day Care. To visitors, staff and patients, the unit appeared calm, tranquil and relaxed creating a restful atmosphere. Matron Barbara Kettley remarked that this kind of atmosphere does not happen by accident:

"A lot of time, thought and energy on the part of myself and all staff goes into the creation of a restful environment, which is so crucial for the well being of our patients and their loved ones. The atmosphere is passionately conserved and any negativity soon disappears if it is discouraged.."

"Tears and laughter abound. *Sadness* and *Celebrations* are all part of the hospice..."

The volunteers that came together during the several years before April 1991, when the hospice opened its doors to patients, were ready to continue committing their skills and time to the hospice. Those who decided to move on from fundraising, offered themselves, from the beginning, to work with the hospice, showing the public around on open days, answering the telephone and decorating the building. These were the nucleus of the large team of volunteers who had become an integral part of the hospice. The interest for volunteering was growing in the community, and Voluntary Services Organiser, Faith Tournay admired volunteers' dedication:

Holistic *care...*

"The volunteers are a caring and committed team, bringing a very personal contribution and contact from the community, which enriches the quality of life in the hospice. Long may they continue to do so."

The hospice's very strong ethos of holistic care under the direction of Barbara Ketley continued in successive years of operation. General Manager from 1994, Martin Johnson said:

"Barbara convened staff meetings every morning which were about thinking time and positive thoughts. It was the sort of thing some people thought of as a little eccentric but it seemed to work. We discovered the various psychological barriers people had to hospice care – that you go to a hospice to die. To this, our response was that our focus was and would always be on helping people while they were living. With the conditions our patients had they would have gone through a lot – perhaps the damaging effects of chemotherapy or radiotherapy – but when they came to us they flourished within the holistic care environment. Even things like the intuitiveness of our catering team – knowing what people wanted to eat and in what portions – made a difference.

"Not having come from a clinical environment, I was keen to observe the impact on patients and I can say I saw people with a prognosis of a day surviving ten days against all expectations, or people with a prognosis of a week surviving months. I even remember one patient with a prognosis of a few months who survived many years, so I could see what an enormous difference this kind of support actually gave and, using modern language, how it empowered people to engage with their own care."

Dr Wink White with the Duchess of Gloucester at the Royal opening in November 1991

Holistic care: patients in a four bedded ward and in the Day Care unit

The Duchess of Gloucester revealing the plaque in the main reception at the Royal opening

The icing on the *cake...*

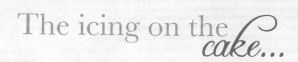

> "It is a wonderful place and I wish everyone who comes to work here and the patients who come in for short-term or long-term stay, all the very best."

The Royal opening event in November 1991 was the pinnacle of the first year. It was a wonderful reward for all the hard work. On a windy and cold day, a crowd of hospice supporters gathered to meet the Duchess of Gloucester and officially mark the opening of the Luton and South Bedfordshire Hospice. A lot of local press attended. Upon arrival, the Duchess of Gloucester was taken on a tour around the hospice, where she chatted to nurses and volunteers, taking her time to ask questions. Welcoming smiles led the Duchess from room to room where she listened to Dr Siegler's comments about the equipment and facilities that the new hospice was now able to offer. The Duchess spent longest talking to one of the patients enquiring about their condition and listening to their praise for the hospice staff. After the tour, the Duchess gave a speech, acknowledging all the hard work that had gone into it:

> *"I just wanted to say thank you very much for inviting me to visit you in this very new hospice. I have heard so much praise for the doctors and nurses who work here. Maybe I expected it to be like that, but it was very very heart warming to hear that from the patients themselves. I do think you have some very good patients too! I would like to congratulate everyone who was involved in making this hospice a possibility and a reality. So many people have worked very hard in raising funds, deciding, planning, building and kitting it absolutely right. It is a wonderful place and I wish everyone who comes to work here and the patients who come in for short-term or long-term stay, all the very best."*

For Dr Siegler, the Royal opening was the key landmark:

> *"The Duchess of Gloucester was terrific. She spoke to every in-patient. She discussed recipes for cakes, and it was just a pleasure to take her around the site. Wink's eyesight was not good enough to get him around and we were told by the Lord Lieutenant there was a time constraint, she had to be in and out in an hour-and-a-half. So I was delegated to walk her through the tour."*

Challenges continue

Once the festivities marking the tremendous first year were over, hospice life started settling down and new priorities were discussed. The hospice's trustee Ron Upton remembered:

> *"The design of the hospice has been praised by all who visit it, by lay people for its comfort and 'friendly atmosphere' and by professionals for its practicality, use of space and the facilities offered...*

> "One patient's relatives said they had never visited a place that was 'less like a hospital', the greatest praise possible as far as we are concerned."

After a hard-earned flying start of the opening year, other challenges for running the hospice and maintaining its high quality of care were still to come. The hospice faced a test to raise a minimum of £500,000 a year to maintain the standards. Ron Upton remarked in 1992:

> *"We have our building, we have our much admired staff and we are building a reputation for excellence among the public and in the medical world. This does not come cheap. We will never be able to thank adequately the people of South Bedfordshire for the hard work they have already put into fundraising and practical help for their hospice, and we know we can rely on their help in the future."*

Hospice 'hasbeens'

meet once again

A group of the hospice's original nurses jokingly call themselves the hospice 'hasbeens' and are to this day a closely knit team. They shared a glimpse of their earliest memories of the hospice:

It was a Monday morning in March, 1991 and the small complement of clerical staff were beavering away on the first floor of the spankingly-brand-new Luton and South Bedfordshire Hospice.

On the ground floor Matron, Barbara Kettley, Charge Nurse, William Randall, and Sister, Jacky Tritton, were waiting to welcome the diverse mix of individuals who had been selected to be the nursing staff of this ground-breaking venture.

We were, without exception, nervously excited and full of anticipation as we each walked through those front doors for the first time. Many of us didn't know anyone else although nurses Ruth and Marian as well as Sarah and Breda were already friends. We were all female, but that is where the likeness ended. We were about sixteen in number, as far as we can recall. Nine or ten were fully-fledged State Registered Nurses with many years of experience under their belts and two were State Enrolled Nurses (a qualification not recognised today). The remainder had no nursing experience at all. Indeed, one of the ladies, Lesley, had a background in retail. She recalls how she walked into the hospice, when it was nearing completion, to have a cup of coffee (how did she have the nerve?). But, as she says, she got the job - that's our Lesley!

'Hasbeen' Ruth recalls meeting Dr. David Seigler (who was to become the Medical Director) for the first time. He was billed to speak about the hospice at a local W.I. meeting, and, although not normally to be seen at the W.I. (much too young!) Ruth and Marian decided to go along. After the meeting, they 'nobbled' David and asked how they could get a job there. Ruth was working in a nursing home at the time and was wearing her uniform under her coat as she was on her way to work, so 'flashed' her uniform at David.

One can only imagine David's response - but it must have impressed him! David teased her about it for many years to come. Most of us, however, went through the normal processes of interviews to be offered our posts. However we came by our positions, every one of us was as proud as punch to have been given this very privileged chance to practice nursing in this wonderful environment.

"We have our building, we have our much admired staff and we are building a reputation for excellence among the public and in the medical world. This does not come cheap. We will never be able to thank adequately the people of South Bedfordshire for the hard work they have already put into fund-raising and practical help their hospice, and we know we can rely on their help in the future."

In a two-week induction programme to give us the very basics of palliative care nursing, whether we were to be working on the In-patient Unit or in Day Hospice.

"We were all to be taking part..."

The course was varied and included external speakers as well as tailor-made specific learning - some of it very daunting, but we were all in the same boat. The bonding began in those early days, supporting and helping each other. We all, of course, had differing strengths and weaknesses but, largely down to the clever recruiting of individuals, friendships, born out of mutual respect, were formed and in many cases last to this day.

We weren't the only 'new kids on the block' back in those pioneering days. We somehow acquired two cats, brother and sister, who were given the names Meg and Alfie. They both lived lives of luxury and longevity and were much loved by cat lovers! Nurse Marian remembers a patient who was admitted for end-of-life care. His wife was very keen on their own pet moggie, so the cat was 'admitted' along with the patient. Marian wasn't, and isn't, a cat lover but had to put aside her dislike of them to lift Meg and Alfie onto the patient's lap - the one and only time she handled those creatures!

As our induction programme came to an end, our minds awash with new knowledge, we were divided into two teams for which the names Alpha and Omega were chosen. Duty rotas were drawn up: the staff were divided between the three shifts covering 24 hours. A normal week for any of the nursing staff would be a mixture of all shifts, which played havoc with family and social life but was accepted as the norm. The eagerly anticipated day dawned when our first patients were due to arrive. Generally we felt ill-equipped individually but need not have feared, as we were fully supported by our senior staff, who were champions at encouraging, teaching and training. Months later, at the official opening, there was much excitement and anticipation amongst us. As the Duchess arrived, a specially chosen little girl advanced to present the royal guest with the obligatory bouquet of flowers. That little girl was the daughter of nurse Marian: Verity was four years old at the time and looked a picture! Apparently she doesn't remember anything about it now but the proud Mum recalls how, as Verity started to get bored waiting, Liz, the chef, produced one of her legendary profiteroles for Verity to enjoy. It was almost bigger than the child!

Our usual nursing day would begin at 7.30 a.m., when the early shift came in and the night shift were often on their knees, needing their beds. A short 'quiet time' had been established to help focus on the day ahead. This was led by a member of the night staff and would embrace a reading of some sort, like a suitable poem or a bible reading. It always included part of the hospice philosophy, again to help us focus on our responsibilities to our patients, their families and to each other.

Another 'quiet time', at 10 a.m. was offered to other staff (clerical, Liz and her team in the kitchen, Angela and her team of housekeepers and the laundry workers). This was often led by Matron or a nurse from the unit and followed a similar format. Anne, a nursing auxiliary on the unit remembers the excellent 'grounding' that was instilled in us by Barbara, the Matron. She facilitated our early learning needs and made sure we had ongoing training to help us keep up with new developments. We all remain very grateful to Barbara for that early discipline.

Some individuals found 'niches' alongside their nursing practice. Lesley, who over a period of time suffered a painful back condition, which some days limited her physically, became an excellent librarian. She established the library and a filing system bit by bit as funds would allow and stocked the shelves with reference books. Ruth and Marian, who job-shared, helped develop Silver Lining, an early a bereavement support service.

There were various options on offer to those who needed help with grief and sadness. Later, another Nurse, Anne, also made a valuable contribution to that team for many years.

"Two annual 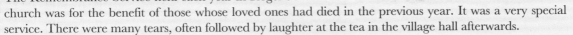vents which were hugely appreciated... "

Two annual events which were hugely appreciated were arranged through Silver Lining. They were supported by local clergy: Rev. Roger Wood, Vicar of Streatley at the time, and Fr. Bernard Hughes, a local Catholic priest who became part of the furniture at the hospice and was well-loved. The Remembrance Service held each year in Roger's church was for the benefit of those whose loved ones had died in the previous year. It was a very special service. There were many tears, often followed by laughter at the tea in the village hall afterwards.

The Lights of Love ceremony, held on the first Sunday in December in the hospice grounds, served a similar purpose. As many nurses as possible, whether on-duty or off, would attend and re-acquaint themselves with familiar faces. It was often the first time some of the families had been back, which made it difficult for them, but very valuable in their ongoing healing of grief.

Part of the nurses' remit in those days was Public Relations. Gill Abbott derived great pleasure in visiting groups in the community to give talks in order to impart knowledge and extract cash! There was a great deal of misunderstanding still at that time about the purpose of hospices, but the talks were always well received. Other occasions were for the sole purpose of receiving cheques and giving the vote of thanks. A stalwart hospice supporter organised a garden party at her home each year for many years: Gill attended a couple of those, in uniform, to mingle and chat. She was responsible for eating all those yummy cakes in order to further the cause, but someone had to do it, didn't they? We were, and are, ordinary people whose personal lives didn't always run smoothly. We were expected to leave those things at the door in order to make room for whatever might come our way during the course of a shift. And some of it was very difficult, but we had an unspoken rule that no one would go off-duty burdened by sadness or grief. We'd always be available for each other.Nursing at the hospice was nursing in it's purest sense: many of us had come from busy working environments and adapting to a slower pace was difficult at first. The nurse to patient ratio was excellent and we were actively encouraged to spend time listening, observing and chatting. The building of relationships with the patients and their families was considered to be as vital as the practical care. Our Matron considered 'time' to be one of the most important aspects of care and it was never to be stinted.

Alongside the very nature of the work, we had enormous fun. The patients and families were often part of the fun, too. Once, Sarah somehow managed to tie Roger Sharpe's shoe laces together while they were talking at the Nurses Station. He, of course, fell over! Then there were times when we used to have wheelchair races down the garden corridor. This could only happen during the evenings when we were sure everyone was off the premises!

'Hasbeen' Ruth is still traumatised by the experience she endured during her final shift before leaving for pastures new. Suffice to say it involved the Jacuzzi bath while she was in full uniform! Fundraising Summer Balls gave us an opportunity to really dress up and enjoy ourselves outside of work and the Barn Dances held at a nearby farm were great fun. Daily laughter, often mixed in with tears – this is what sums up the hospice to us, the 'hasbeens'. Not only laughter on the menu, but romance. Peter was a volunteer receptionist on Sunday afternoons. Nurse Sarah took a shine to him and he took a shine to her. They were married with a bedpan guard of honour and have been making each other happy for about 14 years now!

Twenty one years on from their nervous beginnings, many of the friendships formed among the original nursing team survive. Every few months some of the group gather over food and drinks to reminisce and laugh as we used to. Most are still working in the nursing field and some have been put out to the grassy fields of retirement, but, without exception, every one of us will be eternally grateful for the wonderful experience of those early hospice days. We each individually had much to contribute and there are no doubt some glaring omissions in this account - blame the thinning of the grey cells! Our dear 'hasbeens', we hope you enjoy the read.

"Your contribution to those first years was equally

Valued as are the ongoing

Friendships"

-*Ruth Hammond, Marian Townsend, Gill Abbott,*
Lesley Skerman, Sarah Clark and Ann Bates

Hospice staff in 1991

Not a job but a huge *Privilege*

A personal recollection from the hospice Matron

My father died of lung and kidney cancer when he was 58 years old. I had recently qualified as RGN in my 20s. He died in terrible pain in a busy hospital general ward, without dignity and without his family by his bedside. From that day I vowed I would try to help find a way to enable patients and families towards a pain free, peaceful, dignified life whilst having a terminal illness for however long they had left to live.

As part of my District Nurse training I was seconded, at my request, to St Christopher's Hospice where I met and was tutored by Dame Cecily Saunders – the founder of the Hospice Movement in Great Britain. She was inspirational and confirmed my idea that there must be a better way than my Dad had suffered in his last weeks. Then passion inspired me that patients could enjoy a peaceful, pain free, end of life surrounded by love.

As a District Nurse I was able to care for patients with cancer and other illnesses, in their own home, and developed skills and understanding of the needs of patients and their families through further training in teaching, counseling and cancer care, diagnosis and treatments.

I was appointed as a Macmillan Nurse first at Willen Hospice and then with the Luton and South Bedfordshire Health Authority some years later (1989, August). I was interviewed by Dr David Siegler and Dr Wink White for the post of Matron at the Luton and South Bedfordshire Hospice, and was lucky enough to get the job! I was appointed in November 1989 and was told the hospice was to be opened on April 2nd 1990.

Betty Robinson, who donated the land was kept informed of my appointment and I visited her regularly to keep her updated on the progress. The building was then incomplete, but the roof was on, so together with the architects and Trustees, the building was furnished and equipped in the following months. During the next few months I arranged several 'open days' for the recruitment of staff.

At each event I gave a talk on what the hospice aims were, what the philosophy was and what would be expected of any staff to be appointed. I had put out graded job descriptions, not only for nursing staff, but also for cleaners, kitchen staff, secretaries and instructed interested participants to collect application forms. I had consulted with the HR Department of the Luton & Dunstable Hospital who were enormously helpful to me.

I had been given a Nursing Staff Budget from the Trustees, and planned how many staff and what grades would be needed. Dr David Siegler was Medical Director and he and Dr Wink White appointed the Medical Staff.

My responsibilities were never explicit, so I put together a description of the post of Matron. The Trustees accepted it and gave it their approval. Part of my role was to visit patients that had been referred, either by GPs or hospital doctors, either at their home or in hospital, to inform them and their families what the hospice could offer them, as well as to assess their needs. There were several options offered including hospice admission for symptom control, respite care or terminal care and day care.

I already had plans for a comprehensive bereavement care service at a later date. The first patient I visited at home at the GP's request a few days before the opening of the hospice was a 40 year old mother of 2 (8 and 10 years), who was terminally ill and pleaded to be taken into the hospice to die, as she did not want to die at home, feeling it would traumatise her children.

The hospice was due to open in 2-3 days and I had my doubts if the mother would survive in time to be admitted. She did, and was taken in on April 2nd and was truly grateful. I was called at 3am that night by the lovely Helen to say the lady had died during the night, just as she had wished. Helen and the wonderful nursing assistant cared for her and her family in the way I had hoped.

The lady's husband and the children were the first to be offered bereavement care at the hospice. My personal philosophy of hospice care is one of love. Love should pervade every corner of the building, to be poured out to patients, families, each other and anyone entering the hospice building.

To encourage this I consulted the hospice Chaplains and together we planned a 20 minute quiet time every morning before the day starts, where all staff, volunteers, nursing, admin, kitchen, cleaning, as well as patients and relatives, would meet in the Quiet Room. The aim, to remind us all why we are here and to promote love and support to all. The night staff would have their own quiet time before the day staff came on.

One event that remains in my memory was visiting a gentleman at home who was in severe pain with many other symptoms of a very severe illness and his GP insisted he should be admitted. The patient was angry and in denial of his condition and took a lot of persuading to come in for symptom control. He had fallen out with his only relative – his son, and with most of his neighbours. The man gave the nurses a very hard time. His symptoms were controlled after a few days. Each nurse would come out of his room looking drained, exhausted and often in tears. We even devised shifts so that each nurse would be with him for a couple of hours and then have an hour or two to recover while the next nurse took over. I kept reminding them to just pour love on him, smile, reassure and remain loving.

The patient began to relax after a week or so. I shall never forget the change in him over the next few weeks. He remained with us into his terminal stage and he died with his son and family beside him, peacefully, without distressing symptoms and with a smile on his face!

His son remarked he had never seen his father so happy! Ruth, Marion, Sally, Helen, Lesley and all the staff – too many to mention were remarkably loving, patient, kind, caring and saw him through with total commitment.

Another event that has always stayed with me is the day that five of our terminally ill patients died in one day – on one shift, from 7.30am - 3.30pm. Every patient, every member of the five families had 100% care, love, support, skilled nursing and one-to-one attention. The nurses and volunteers were amazing.

Ruth was on that shift and I remember she and I walked around the garden at the end of that day, crying and happy that not one patient or members of their family missed out in any way, despite the intense situation. Calmness and love ruled that day.

Faith Tournay, Volunteer Organiser, was a very valued member of the early team. She took on and supervised and trained up to 400 volunteers. Without these wonderful selfless people, the nursing staff would be under enormous pressure and would find days like the 'five deaths on one shift' impossible to sustain or get through. The volunteers kept everyone going with tea, sandwiches, clearing tables and dozens of quiet unasked for tasks performed with quiet love and dignity.

I could fill pages with examples of how the hospice volunteers enabled the staff to give our patients and their families all they deserve. Faith Tournay and Roger Sharp were instrumental in upholding and enabling the Hospice to gain a reputation that was second to none in the Hospice Movement. Their work in fundraising and using and helping and inspiring volunteers was remarkable.

Dr David Siegler and Dr Wink White and Betty Robinson were the backbone in the early days of the hospice. Dr Siegler was always there when needed and despite a very busy life as a consultant physician at the hospital, always visited the hospice every day. I always thought of Dr Wink White as the 'Father' of the hospice, as without him and David Siegler it would not have come about.

My passion...

My passion for delivery of excellence of nursing care to patients and families still motivates me. Many of my staff have said to me in the past: 'This is why I came into nursing'.

I am saddened to hear of the poor standards of nursing care delivered to patients in some of our hospitals. The hospice movement stands out as a model of care for all, not only terminally ill patients. I sincerely hope Keech Hospice Care continues to deliver love and care and long may it do so.

" I could fill pages...

with examples of how the hospice volunteers enabled the staff to give our patients and their families

all they deserve."

Matron Barbara Kettley in 1991

There are so many people, staff, patients, relatives and friends made, whom I shall never forget and will be forever grateful to them for making the role of Matron for me not a job – but a huge privilege. I was sad to leave, but knowing that people there – including of course Janet and Meg and many more, would carry on with the hospice philosophy, eased the pain of leaving.

I wish Keech Hospice Care success and continuity of the love and care which is so needed by the local population, whose hospice it is – after all!

Barbara Kettley
(Hospice Matron from 1989 - 1997)

Barbara Kettley with Betty Robinson at the hospice celebration

Chapter Six

Three years, three firsts

"With the aim of building up a consistent source of income, the charity opened its first shop in 1993."

Between 1993 and 1996, as the adult hospice began to grow and develop, the charity's management team were looking carefully into a range of new ideas that could boost income. The discussions which took place then led to the development of the hospice shops, the Keech lottery and the charity's Smiley Sam Christmas float. Over the years, these different fundraising activities have prospered and whether the public has been drawn to the idea of finding a bargain, winning big or seeing Santa, all three have proved incredibly popular and lucrative!

Success in store

With the aim of building up a consistent source of income, the charity opened its first shop in 1993. The shop at Ashton Square, Dunstable was shortly joined by a second outlet which opened in 1994 in the Arndale Centre, Luton. At that time, the retail side of the charity was also selling items of furniture through its warehouse in Selbourne Road, Luton and had two vans at its service. Driven by volunteers, these were available to collect bulky items that donors were unable to bring to the shops and managed the transportation of goods from shops to the warehouse for sorting and redistribution. A third shop in Sundon Park, Luton opened in 1995 and since then the charity's retail arm has continued to grow and grow and grow. At the time of publishing this book, there are now 25 Keech shops located far and wide across Bedfordshire, Hertfordshire and the Milton Keynes area. The first phase of expansion came between 1995 and 2008 when, Joan Gray, Administration and Finance Manager at the time, helped the charity grow its shops from two to nine outlets. Recalling that time, she commented:

"... When I first joined the hospice, the shops were in a very embryonic stage. Martin Johnson and I made it our aim to keep going for new shops and that's what we did. By the time we'd got up to ten shops the whole operation needed a stronger backing team in terms of management and administration. It's good to see what was put into place."

Martin Johnson added:

"To start with we didn't expect to make any kind of quick profits but the retail side of the charity took off really well. After I had left the charity I was pleased to see that by around 2003 the shops were making significant profits for the charity. A lot of that was initially due to Joan Gray. Her attention to detail and lifelong experience of running shops was invaluable to the charity.

"Seeing how well the shops are doing today shows that developing this side of the charity was the right thing to do. They bring in a much more durable type of income – independent from political interference and the unpredictability of grant making trusts. I remember feeling, around the time of the Millennium, very let down by two or three major trusts who decided they wanted to fund buildings but not the services that operated within them. And, although it was no surprise, we'd also faced a series of let downs by the NHS. In contrast, the income coming in from shops didn't look like it was going to let us down and seeing the profits they make today that has certainly been proved correct!"

A *Blaze* leads to something **new**

In February 2002, hospice staff were stunned to hear that the charity's warehouse at Selbourne Road, Luton had gone up in flames. Fire-fighters from Luton, Stopsley, Dunstable and Kempston took several hours to put out the blaze which held strong into the early hours of Thursday 7th February that year. The fire, which was believed to have started in a van parked in the building, caused irreparable damage to the warehouse and an estimated £100,000 loss in donated goods for the hospice.

While the news came as a terrible shock, as on so many other occasions, the resourcefulness of people at the hospice came into play. The disaster was briefly mourned but quickly turned into an opportunity as a new and better warehouse was found and secured for the charity by trustee, Jack Sapsworth.

Joan Gray remembers hearing the news:

Joan Gray

"I was on my way to London for a meeting when I got a call to say there had been a fire at the warehouse. So I literally got off one train and straight on another back to Luton to find the warehouse totally burnt out. Forensics came out and it was really quite a shock for us to see such damage. But, we were very fortunate that, with the help of Jack Sapsworth, we found another warehouse quite quickly on Leagrave Road. It was actually a much better space which the charity still uses today so in the end everything worked out well."

The charity's warehouse at Leagrave Road

Donations flood in a fire hits hospice stor

BY ALISON KNIBB

STAFF at the trouble-hit Pasque Hospice have been overwhelmed by the support they have received after fire ripped out around £80,000 worth of donated goods.

The adult and children's hospice in Great Bramingham Lane, Luton, has been inundated with calls from supporters offering donations and practical help.

The fire at the hospice's only warehouse in Selbourne Road in the early hours of Thursday morning destroyed all the stock for the nine Pasque shops.

Furniture sold from there was also smoke damaged.

Fire-fighters from Luton, Stopsley, Dunstable and Kempston took five hours to put out the blaze, which is believed to have been caused by an electrical fault in a delivery van parked in the building.

While many staff members and volunteers were reduced to tears when they heard the news, the mood has since changed, with the community rallying round to help.

ALL STOCK GONE: The scene at the hospice's Selbourne Road warehouse.

John Quill, the hospice's chief executive, told *The Luton News*: "The fire is obviously a big blow to us, particularly as we were storing up all the spring stock, so all the spring fashion's gone.

"But we have been inundated with offers of help, which is great.

"Since I announced the hospice was in a difficult financial position last year, the turnout at our shops has been terrific and we hope that will continue despite this setback. We are very grateful to all the people who have been calling and are sorry that it has taken us a couple of days to get

organised but we are now in a position to take donated goods.

Two vans have been loaned to the hospice to collect goods - two of its vans were destroyed in the blaze. Beech Hill Conservative Club has offered to store goods for the hospice while they sort out alternative accommodation.

Mr Quill said: "Luton Round Table have been active on our behalf and as a result we have seen a warden on the Britannia Estate while, with a fair wind, we could be in a couple of weeks time. Beech Hill Conservative Club has offered to help meanwhile, but we don't want people turning up there with goods. Anything small, like clothes, can be taken to our shops and if anyone has bigger items, we are asking them to phone the hospice or their local hospice shop to arrange collection.

To add to the hospice's misery, money was stolen from offices at the hospice shop in Ashton Square, Dunstable, on Friday afternoon.

A thief broke into the upstairs offices, taking cash from employees' purses, while a customer, believed to be an accomplice, chatted to staff downstairs.

Warehouse fire, as reported in the Luton News

At the end of 2006, the hospice's retail arm was overseen by what was then a separate entity from the charity, the Pasque Trading Company. At the same time, volunteer Pat Jefferson, who had spent several years helping to clean the changing rooms and the floor in the swimming pool, was looking for a change of direction. Knee replacement surgery meant he could no longer fulfil this role but, because of his previous business experience, Pat was invited by Chief Executive, John Quill to join the board of the Trading Company.

John had, at this time, also employed the services of a consultant firm to look at various aspects of the hospice. When they examined the retail side of the charity, they concluded that it was underperforming compared to other charity retail outlets, both on turnover and profitability.

In September 2007, two members of the Trading Company – Chairman Jack Sapsworth and MD Joan Gray – stepped down. Pat Jefferson, who took over as Chairman, said:

> "It was very evident that we needed a Retail Manager who could increase the performance and expand our retail activities. During the recruitment period I was thankful for the advice and help offered by Joan Gray and for the support given by former Retail Operations Manager, Paul Scrivener, who came out of retirement to help. Eventually we found Philip Kojcinovic who joined us in February 2008 and has helped to expand the number of shops significantly."

Today, the reputation of Keech's 25 charity shops for high quality and great value is such that whenever a new opening is announced, local shoppers turn up in droves and are frequently seen queuing down the street! The best news for the charity, of course, is that such success means the income raised through the shops has rapidly escalated. In 2011, it reported record profits of £968,000, an increase of over 200% from the previous year!

In 2008, the charity introduced Gift Aid into its shops, enabling them to reclaim tax money on the value of donations brought into the shops and creating another superb source of income. Out of that record amount raised in 2011, £120,000 came through Gift Aid.

Inside the Harpenden home charity shop

" I was thankfull...

for the advice and help offered
by Joan Gray and for the
support given by former
Retail Operations Manager,
Paul Scrivener, who came out
of retirement

to help. "

While its shops continue to offer a variety of donated and new goods, the charity has made some radical changes to ensure each of its outlets is appealing and welcoming to a modern customer.

Now with 11 shops in Bedfordshire, seven in Hertfordshire and three in the vicinity of Milton Keynes, Keech has also diversified its retail business in recent years, with the opening of stores devoted to a specific type of goods. A large outlet selling furniture opened in Stopsley, Luton in January 2010 and a store dedicated to a stylish range of home interiors opened in Harpenden in July 2011.

Philip Kojcinovic spoke of his aspirations for the future:

"It's been very rewarding to see the expansion plans put into place and to see income go up so dramatically but there's still more to do. In our 21st year we're aiming for profits over the million pound mark and...

" ...In three years time...

I'd like to see Keech credited as having the most
profitable hospice charity shops in the country! "

Roll up, Roll up

Keech lottery leaflet

The Millennium Lottery
Draw, December 1999

Boxer Billy Schwer
(right) helping to
promote the lottery.
Courtesy of John
Shorthouse LBIPP

In 1995, the charity began discussing the idea of running a weekly lottery, charging £1 a go, or a 'chance', as they say in the business. At the time, the UK's National Lottery was hitting the headlines for paying large amounts of money to what a large proportion of the public deemed to be not particularly worthy causes. For example, this was the year in which a furore arose over the purchase of the Churchill archive with £12.5 million of National Lottery Funds, after which the all-party Commons Heritage Select Committee began a formal investigation into the way lottery grants were handed out.

With such negative press in the back of his mind, General Manager at the hospice, Martin Johnson explained how the decision to begin a hospice lottery was not taken lightly:

"I had a kind of ethical ambivalence to the idea of a lottery but I thought it through and I could think of several advantages our lottery had over the National Lottery primarily that all the money from ours would be going towards patient care. I was really pleasantly surprised at how well this lottery took off."

The brainchild of fundraiser, Roger Sharp, there was a lot to do before the lottery could be launched. A licence was needed from South Bedfordshire District Council and some further decisions had to be made about whether to pay an external operator or work in-house to run the lottery and about what the prize fund should be. After considering the options and the costs involved, Keech decided to run the entire operation itself and offer a total prize fund of £1,500. With an initial team of two – George Pearce, the Lottery Promoter and Paul Denton, running the administration – a launch date was set for 5th April 1996.

The next task was to make sure enough £1 tickets were sold, in order to cover the prize fund, together with all of the other operating costs. It didn't take a degree in mathematics to figure out that if the hospice only sold a few hundred tickets and had to pay out £1,500 in prize monies, a substantial loss could be looming. Thankfully this was far from the case as the inaugural draw saw £3,274 made in ticket sales and a net profit of £1,774. Not bad for a first effort! From the very start, a network of lottery collectors and canvassers was recruited. As a result of this, weekly membership soon exceeded 4,000, a level it remained steady at for a number of years. After the opening of the children's hospice, Keech decided to duplicate its lottery efforts to raise revenue for the children's service throughout Hertfordshire. With a specific remit to develop this, Richard Field joined the team. He remembers:

"At the time I joined, The Comet newspaper had chosen Keech Cottage Children's Hospice as its charity of the year and were featuring readers' fundraising ideas and events each week. At the same time, we recruited a new canvasser, Barbara Saunders and a collector Ted Bishopp, who both lived in Stevenage. With all of this promotional activity taking place, our ticket sales soon began to increase and, within a few years, weekly player numbers had soared through the 10,000 barrier."

Two ladies who have helped to sell a large quantity of those tickets over the years are volunteers Dorothy Cullen and Beryl Roadnight. Having hosted many a stall at fêtes and fairs to promote the lottery over the years, Dorothy explained that the secret to making a sale is all in the talk:

> "Well, if I see someone coming towards me with a dog, first of all I will talk to the dog and then the lady. Sometimes they will end up buying two tickets instead of one. It works with children as well! The other thing is I love names so I'll often ask people what their surname is and we'll have a chat about names. Once, when we were out in Sundon Park we came across four Australian ladies and two men and they brought about five tickets – all because we were interested in where they came from."

Another long-standing volunteer, Sue Garden, has proved invaluable to the lottery team helping in the office over the years. While the workings of the hospice lottery have essentially remained the same, over the years it has had to take account of new legislation such as the Gambling Act in 2005 and take on various new ideas. One of those winning ideas was to introduce a bumper draw in December 1999 with an increased prize fund of £5,500. Originally branded as the Millennium Draw for that first year, by 2001 the draw had been moved to June and became known as the Midsummer Draw. To this day it still raises in excess of £30,000 each year. In October 2003, the lottery got a face-lift. The weekly prize structure was increased by £500, creating a total prize fund of £2,000 spread across 40 cash prizes. In the same year it also began promoting lottery membership as a unique gift for Christmas and introduced a 'Snowy bear' toy which was sent as an extra thank you to anyone who purchased a gift over £25.

15 years on...

Jump ahead to 2011 and the Keech Hospice Care lottery was celebrating two special occasions to mark its longevity – its 15th anniversary draw on 5th April and then its 800th draw on 29th July. To celebrate the 15th anniversary draw, original team members, George Pearce and Paul Denton, returned to the hospice to present the £1,000 jackpot to the lucky winners, pensioners Brian and Dorothy Horton. The couple were delighted to hear of their win, which came the day before Brian celebrated his 74th birthday. Dorothy commented:

> ## "The hospices do such good work for the community and playing this lottery is a really easy way for us to do something to help."

> " I don't know why but I had a kind of premonition that we were going to win this week and I kept looking out for the postman! Lucky for us that premonition came true!"

For the 800th draw, the top prize went to Lin Pratt who bought her winning ticket in the charity's Dunstable shop located at Ashton Square. She was presented with her winnings at the shop on Monday 1st August by Shop Manager, Jacqui Marstin alongside the very first member of the lottery, Mrs Eileen Kitsell. Lin said:

> "When I got the call to say I had won, I took a bit of convincing that it was actually true, but obviously I was delighted! Whenever I'm in Dunstable I pay a visit to the Keech shop as there's always so much to choose from and I'm very glad I popped in and bought that lottery ticket now! I've already got a holiday planned in Menorca so it will be lovely to have this extra spending money."

Luckily for Keech, its weekly lottery continues to thrive. In 2011, it passed the £6 million mark in the total it has raised for the hospices during its lifetime and achieved a peak of almost 12,000 weekly ticket sales. Even with the prize fund of £2,000 that makes a very significant surplus towards the two hospice's annual funding requirements.

Fundraising Director, Jacqui Shepherd, commented:

"This a truly remarkable sum and shows the continued support of our wonderful community."

In recent years, the Keech Hospice Care lottery further developed the idea of memberships as gifts for any special occasion and in February 2011, it broadened its product again with the introduction of specially packaged £1 tickets for use as wedding favours. Current Senior Lottery Administrator at the charity, Liz Gallagher commented:

"Our wedding favours make unique little gifts for guests and, with every one given the chance to win up to £1,000, that's got to be better than a few sugared almonds! We've already seen a really positive response and are looking forward to seeing a wedding guest win big soon. We always love seeing the faces of our jackpot winners and get great satisfaction in seeing the funds go across to the two hospice services each week."

"Luckily for Keech,

it's weekly lottery continues to thrive. In 2011, it passed the £6 million mark in the total it has raised for the hospices during its lifetime and achieved a peak of almost 12,000 weekly

ticket sales."

Jacqui Marstin, Lin Pratt and Eileen Kitsell at the presentation of the 800th lottery winner's cheque

Smiley Sam

Santa and Smiley Sam get
to work

Back in 1995, a Community Fundraising Committee made up of twelve people, was helping the charity to look into different fundraising schemes. Taking inspiration from the Rotary Club of Watford North project he had previously been involved in, one of the committee members, Richard Field, put forward the idea of having a Christmas collection around various streets of Luton, accompanied by Father Christmas.

Richard and other committee members spent some time researching the idea further, looking into possible street routes, how to find willing volunteers, what licences would be required and whether there were other local charities working on similar ideas. In doing so, they found out that the two Round Tables which operated in Luton were attempting to cover most of the town, but the smaller of the clubs, Luton Central Round Table, were only heading out each week-end evening throughout December. Their float was in the form of a wooden steam engine, mounted on a trailer borrowed from the local Sea Scouts and towed by a brand new Vauxhall Omega estate car, kindly loaned to them by Vauxhall.

"I chose *the name* which resonated with what we were doing...

When Christmas was over, the float was taken off the trailer and stored under the Arndale Centre throughout the rest of the year.

Luton Central Round Table very kindly agreed that Keech could borrow their float during week-day evenings and so, it came to pass that in December 1996, hospice volunteers were able to go out over a period of two weeks on its first ever Christmas collection. Richard recalls:

"I managed to secure enough volunteers to collect each side of the float and play Father Christmas, leaving me to drive the vehicle. We set a target of raising £3,000 and our final figure at the end of Christmas Eve turned out to be just over that at £3,300. What a success!"

The following year, the charity repeated the same exercise and, with a few extra streets added to the rounds and a few extra volunteers on board, the collections raised a total of £5,500. Seeing the potential this had, in both raising money for the hospice and generating some very valuable publicity too, Richard, sought permission from the General Manager, Martin Johnson, for the charity to purchase its own trailer.

Permission was granted and the trailer was duly bought from Blaines Trailers, based in Little Gaddesden. At the time, a volunteer carpenter, who worked occasional days at the hospice, kindly agreed to construct a wooden steam train to fit on top of the trailer. Once that was built, builders' merchants, Butterfields, supplied one its large crane lorries to lift the huge wooden float and secure it onto the trailer. Richard said:

"What a day that was. We had our lovely new float but then realised it didn't have a name. So, I organised a competition for local boys and girls to name the train and, thanks to the generosity of McDonald's, we had £50 of vouchers to give away as the 1st prize for the best name. The competition was featured in the local paper and several hundred youngsters submitted their names. Eventually I chose the name which resonated with what we were doing and easily rolled off the tongue – 'Smiley Sam'. Well, he did have a nice face painted on the front of his engine!"

Choosing the name presented another problem though – the threat of being sued by the copyright holders of Thomas the tank engine. Imagining the publicity that would come from headlines such as 'Thomas the Tank sues children's hospice', the hospice's response was something along the lines of 'let them sue and see where it gets them'.

...and easily rolled off the tongue - 'Smiley Sam"

Eventually however, common sense prevailed and the copyright holders turned out to be lovely people who showered Keech Cottage with lots of lovely gifts for the children. As the years progressed, sadly both Round Table clubs in Luton folded, leaving the entire town of Luton available to be covered by Smiley Sam at Christmas time. Of course, it has never been possible to cover every street, but to this day, Smiley Sam still does its best!

The idea of adding day-time collections at supermarkets first came about many years back, when hospice supporter, Derrick Dimmock helped the charity make an approach to Asda in Wigmore, Luton, to seek permission to take Smiley Sam there for a few days just before Christmas. This was another huge success and raised between £600- £700 each day!

That set the seeds for further static collections and it was not long before Smiley Sam was working day and night throughout December – taking in the street rounds by night and various supermarkets by day, including Tesco at Hemel Hempstead, Asda at Stevenage, Sainsbury at St Albans and Tesco in Dunstable.

As well as helping Keech to initiate those first supermarket collections with Smiley Sam, Derrick was also one of the many local people who took the role of Father Christmas. For many years, Derrick became Santa for the longest route, in Stopsley, on Christmas Eve – starting at 5pm and usually running until at least 9pm. The vehicle driver on this route, Richard Field, commented:

"Once it rained so hard all night that none of the children could get out of their homes to see him. Poor Derrick was left to walk the entire four mile route in the pouring rain, walking up drive-ways to meet the children. Every so often I saw him tip up his boots and let the water gush out. But how the children loved it; how much did the parents enjoy seeing their little one's faces; and how glad was I to be driving that night!"

John Maddox remembers another occasion when Smiley Sam caused some alarm to an unsuspected Luton petrol station attendant:

"It was around 2003 and there were about seven of us out with Richard Field as the driver. It wasn't a very good night weather-wise. There were snow flurries and it was bitingly cold so we had all put elf hats on to keep warm. We were somewhere near the New Bedford Road area when the generator on the engine went. That also meant the lights went out.

"The nearest petrol station wasn't too far so there we were, a ghostly spectacle of an engine going down the A6 with seven elves hanging on to the back."

"We glided into the garage and as Richard pulled up, all of us elves jumped off. Well, I think we gave the poor guy behind the counter at the station the shock off his life! Some of us went in with Richard to help calm him down. I remember Jim Hammersley (one of the elves) who thought it was one of the funniest things he'd ever seen."

Today, the Smiley Sam operation has been built up by the fundraising team so much that it now needs over 1200 volunteer hours and raises something in the region of £30-£40,000 each Christmas.

In 2009 and 2010, Smiley Sam hit some trouble with bad weather. In both years, snow and ice made it too dangerous for collectors to go out in the evenings on a number of occasions. That meant the amount of funds collected those years took a dip, but safety came first.

Aside from this, and after only having to be rebuilt once, the investment in a bit of old wood, paint and a trailer has proven to be one of the hospice's best investments! Smiley Sam is now a much loved feature of local life.

In the 21st year of the hospice's history, it is some achievement that its shops have been running for eighteen of those years, its lottery for sixteen years and its Smiley Sam float for seventeen years.

Today, all three continue to go from strength to strength and, although running a chain of shops is nothing like running a lottery or going out on a Christmas float, there is one thing these things all have in common – the dedication and support of the local community. Jacqui Shepherd, Fundraising Director at the charity today, commented:

Smiley Sam grounded by bad weather in 2009

66 Sometimes people think their contribution is small or perhaps insignificant – they may have put a few coins in a collection tin, paid a £1 for a lottery ticket or perhaps donated a few unwanted items to one of our shops. But those 'small' contributions make a huge impact. Because of them, our Smiley Sam float continues to raise thousands every Christmas; the lottery has raised over £6million during its lifetime; and our chain of Keech shops looks set to break £1 million profits a year! 99

What began as ideas and discussions all those years ago now play a major role in raising funds for Keech and a major role in local life.

Tales from behind
the counter

From the earliest hospice shop in Dunstable with its 19 year history to the newest of the Keech charity shops, all have a story to tell. With the number of people and amount of goods that pass through their doors, these stories alone could make up several volumes of this book. Not wishing to create such a tome, here are just some of those stories – told through the recollections of four of the current shop managers.

The first of many

Trading since 1993, the Dunstable shop at Ashton Square has seen many changes, the most recent of which came after current manager, Jacqui Marstin, came to post in 2009. Remembering her first day, Jacqui says the shop at that time was at rock bottom, but that left only one way for it to go – up.

> "My first day was a real eye opener. It was August but the door to the shop was shut, four bored faces greeted me from the desk and there was not a customer to be seen. My first thought was to run, but I made it to the back stock room and up the stairs. That day was the start of the great Dunstable clear out. I left the shop at 9pm and the rest is history, I hope a good history as we now make a profit on a regular basis. It's still hard work, something that everyone should try for a day, but I love it."

Dunstable is a small town which has a central crossroads, through which passes the A5 Watling Street, the first Roman Road to be built in England. Jacqui regrets that, even with such thoroughfares running through it, what was once clearly a thriving little town sadly now has numerous empty shops on its High Street. Despite this, she speaks proudly of the way the shop has prospered with the help of her team of 20 volunteers, saying:

> "It's hard work keeping the place going, but I think that people now see us as a destination shop and not just a shop they stumble across and this is down to the changes that have been made by retail management. I think we have all realised that the charity sector has changed and we now have to compete with mainstream stores. We've done that by a change of attitude, by changing the way that we display our goods and by an overall revamp of the charity shops. There's no more dingy shops for us. We're bright, light and clean with happy staff that I involve as much as I can in the running of the shop. After all I can't do the job without them."

Ashton Square shop as it used to be

"People now see us as a destination shop and *not just a shop* they stumble across."

Fire & fortune

Opening some 14 years after the original hospice shop, the Kempston shop has another story to tell. As one of the first to trade purely to raise funds for the children's hospice, the shop has seen some highs and lows – of exceptional donations and rising income alongside fires and other challenges. Like many others, the shop's Manager, Tracey Smith, began as a volunteer.

"I never knew when I started as a volunteer at the shop, what a change it would make to my life. Within a few months I got to meet so many lovely people in my community that I had not spoken to in the twenty years I had lived in the area. Working with a magnificent team of volunteers and Emma as my assistant, the shop has gone from strength to strength and we now make four times the income that the shop used to take. We have so many fantastic donors and customers that become a second family and you worry if you do not see them."

Unluckily, the shop has faced two fires in its lifetime, firstly when its storage shed was set alight, ruining all of the donations inside and damaging the back of the shop and secondly when the shop's two bins were burnt to the ground at a cost of £800 to replace. As for the donations received at the shop, Kempston has had its share of the unusual, the horrid, the exciting and the extremely generous. Tracey commented:

"There have been many surprises in the donated bags I have opened, for example people's medication and items that would be more suitable in an Ann Summers shop. However one day, after going through a box with mouse droppings in it, I pulled out some folded trousers and found an envelope addressed to Keech. Inside was £500 in cash. I have no idea who the very generous donor was but it really made my day. I have met so many inspiring people and I cannot imagine working anywhere else. Only last Friday a lady walked into the shop, placed an envelope on the counter, did not speak and walked out. When my volunteer gave the envelope to me, it contained a bankers draft for £2,000 to Keech – what more can I say."

The Kempston Shop

Cancer, Comfort, Customers & Chip pans

Over in Hemel Hempstead, the charity's shop opened in June 2009 but Manager, Jeanette Coulter, first became acquainted with Keech in 2001 when her Mum was diagnosed with bowel cancer and came under the care of the hospice. Jeanette remembers:

"I was Mum's full-time carer and sometimes, when I needed to talk to someone outside the family, the staff were always there. That was such a comfort for me and the family. When the time came, mum asked to go into the hospice and her last days were spent with care and dignity, giving our family some precious time to just be there with her. The day she passed away wasn't easy but our last memories are of a very dignified ending to a truly wonderful lady."

Soon after her mother's death, Jeanette began volunteering at the hospice shop in Katherine Drive, Dunstable. Now, as Manager of the Hemel Hempstead shop, Jeanette remembers well some of the more 'interesting' people and donations she's come across:

"I have a wonderful Assistant Manager and a great team of volunteers. We are situated on the high street and have a steady stream of customers throughout the day.

❝ One chap thought it was OK to try trousers on in the middle of the shop. He seemed to think we had seen all he had before but I can assure you we hadn't! ❞

"There was another customer who left all their old clothes in the changing room and walked out wearing our stock – not paid for I might add! As for donated goods, we've had all sorts – chip pans complete with used oil, false teeth – the list is endless. But, on the other side people are very generous and donate really lovely items which we are so very grateful for."

The Happiest shop in town

Whilst all of the Keech shops get on with their primary job of raising funds for the hospices, for many, what happens inside goes much further and, in many ways, each shop has created its own focal point in the community. For the Hitchin shop, which opened in November 2008, this has involved helping the homeless and unemployed make a successful re-entry into work. Manager since May 2010, Belinda Dhillon explains:

"All our volunteers are fantastic but we're really pleased to have had many success stories with gentlemen from the local homeless shelter, The Sanctuary, who have volunteered with us and then found employment. There was Peter who now works as a hotel porter in Welwyn, after being homeless for 9 months and Jarrad who was made homeless at the age of 18 due to family problems but has now joined the army. Then there was 'Ten Foot Tall Paul' (he's only 6' 7" but nothing rhymes with that) who was homeless for two years but is now back in the window fitting industry and is also in a relationship with another of our former volunteers – a totally happy ending."

With such good work going on behind its doors, the shop has also become well-known for its fun and friendly atmosphere. Belinda added:

"We have customers who say that we are the happiest shop in Hitchin and if there was a competition we would win hands down. This could be due to our regular Wednesday aerobics classes that we hold and our dress-up day each Saturday! We do not need an excuse to dress up!"

Since the hospice opened its first shop, the environment in which UK charity shops operate has been challenged in many ways. In recent years alone, charity shops have had to deal with bogus collectors; the competitive 'value' ranges available in major supermarkets; the rise of the 'everything for a pound' culture on the High Street and the added distraction that has come from internet sites that offer means of buying, selling or passing on unwanted items such as eBay, Freecycle, Preloved and others.

To survive in this increasingly competitive market, charity shops today have to offer modern interiors, interesting displays and high standards of customer service. Having revamped its older stores and brought a fresh design to its newer outlets, the 21 Keech Hospice Care shops have borne witness to this.

As a member of both the Charity Retail Association and Help the Hospice's Retail Group, the charity is focused on ensuring its retail operation is run efficiently. Income is maximised in many ways – from improved ranges of seasonal items and the introduction of electrical goods to making the most of Gift Aid donations and increased rag trade prices.

Sourcing locations of new shops is also something the charity has become very proficient at in recent years. When looking for a location, Keech liaises with professional surveyors and carries out a number of checks before agreeing a rental. This includes analysing the competition in terms of other charity and discount retailers, researching the pedestrian flow, checking the square footage of the unit (ideally looking for a minimum of 1200 sq ft) and ensuring parking is available for donation drops. All in all, what were once seen in as the domain of the elderly and the student population, are now visited by a much wider mix of people of all ages and from all sorts of backgrounds. What this eclectic group have in common is the desire to make a purchase that provides great value for money while supporting a cause they care about. While that support continues, every day will bring a new tale and the Keech Hospice Care charity shops will continue to create their own history as the public face of the hospice.

"We have customers who say that *We are* the happiest shop in *Hitchin* „

The Hitchin shop

Mike Penning MP at the Hemel shop opening

" *Every day* brings a new tale. The Keech Hospice Care charity shops continue to create their own history as the public face of the hospice."

Chapter Seven

The hospice's big sister

" I'm surprised how beautiful it looks. It looks as though it's always been there. "

In the spring of 1996, there came another chapter in the history of the hospice. The Day Hospice was built and opened its doors – a move that would treble the number of people who would benefit from the services – all in just under five years since the hospice started.

"I'm *Surprised* how *beautiful* it looks."

The idea to offer day care for palliative patients was born almost simultaneously with the idea to build a local hospice. The initial building was built with this in mind and provided day care facilities from the start, but an extension was long awaited. Just over five years on, the building seemed to have outgrown its initial offering and therefore the new bigger extension was needed. With the building complete, the moving had begun. By the end of January 1996 the transition to the new unit was complete. The superb physiotherapy facilities, treatment rooms, therapy areas and bathing and hairdressing facilities were just some of the improvements which the patients would be enjoying in the new unit. A then trustee, John Maddox, remembered:

> "The extension was much needed by nursing staff and other staff members, some of whom were in temporary buildings to the rear of the adult unit. The Powdrill Centre (as it became known after the opening by Her Majesty's Lord Lieutenant of Bedfordshire, Mr S C Whitbread, JP) was not only a great resource to all onsite staff but also enshrined in perpetuity the parents family name of Marjorie Steel whose own Trust had already played such a philanthropic part in the early days. The Steel Charitable Trust would go on with their vital financial support in the years ahead, with their contribution now totalling £780,000. The official opening was a great cause for celebration and Patrons, Companions of Honour, volunteers, staff and representatives of suppliers, contractors and the local Health Services were all present."

A friend of the hospice who attended the official opening of the new wing, named the Powdrill Centre, remarked:

> "I'm surprised how beautiful it looks. It looks as though it's always been there."

Many gains were about to come from the new expansion. There were people who had needed hospice care and for some reason did not receive it and were slipping through the net. During the opening, Matron Barbara Kettley remarked:

> "The new Powdrill Centre looks like our original hospice's big sister who should always have been there. With the extended services we hope that the net is closing so that no one who needs hospice care is denied it. We, staff and volunteers, all contribute to maintaining the loving, caring atmosphere in fulfilling our hospice philosophy, and making it come alive every single day."

The Day Hospice now offered physiotherapy clinics in groups and individually, aromatherapy, reflexology, massage, hairdressing, manicure and a chance for patients to socialise and use the creativity within, that might have previously been hidden. Mary Wang, one of the early Day Hospice volunteers, remembers:

"I volunteered in the Day Centre in my early twenties for a few months, and it was a very moving experience. I was deeply touched by the dignity with which everyone was treated; there was a real sense of love and care. The patients joined in a range of activities from having their hair styled, to manicures, and one day a trained dog was taken round for people to stroke. The staff showed great patience in helping those who found it hard to communicate, or who needed support in other ways. When I first visited I thought there might be a sad atmosphere there all the time, but I realised there was often laughter to be heard and light-hearted moments in amongst the sadness. And, as time went on, I saw that many people there were focusing on living and loving, on valuing the time they had. I am most grateful for my time there."

A staff nurse, Maria Marshall, was first a nurse in the In-patient Unit and after a couple of years moved to the Day Hospice, not long after the new extension opened. During her eight years with the hospice a lot happened, grew and changed, and it all certainly left a mark on Maria. The first impressions of the hospice were the ones that stayed with Maria until now:

"Since I started working here, I felt the hospice was similar to the one in Kent, but also very very different. There was a more pastoral, spiritual feeling about it. I felt the hospice had a more gentle approach, it was more family-like."

Maria has the experience to compare the differences between nursing in the In-patient Unit and the Day Hospice. The main change for Maria was the purpose: the nurses and volunteers were focusing on maintaining their patients' care they receive at home. Along with medical services like blood transfusions and medication control,

the Day Hospice provided comforting services for the patients like relaxation therapies and health advice related to their illness. Maria commented:

"Volunteers were mostly responsible for the comforting therapies, but they were also our eyes and ears among the patients. We would find out who is having a hard time and many more unexpected details about their lives that sometimes would help us with treating their conditions."

Maria's typical day as the Day Hospice Team Leader, would start with reviewing the list of patients coming in that day and briefing the volunteers.

"There was always the unexpected in the Day Hospice. A crisis would occur and we would just have to deal with it as we went."

The best memory for Maria was meeting the special people:

"There was a sense of achievement among staff and supporters, a truly celebratory atmosphere. I met lots of wonderful friends that I still keep in touch with. It's always a treat to visit a hospice and meet people I've worked with.

"It was never a chore to come to work. I always enjoyed being a nurse and we used to have such a laugh here with the other nurses.

"I've always felt that local people know well and are fond of their local hospice. I think the profile of hospices in general has risen since I first started, as people have a better awareness of what a hospice is. It's first and foremost a part of the community."

" The most enjoyable ones from the early 1990s were making the patients in Day Hospice feel at home..."

Maria remembered that the Day Hospice patients used to regularly be invited to attend publicity events, openings and fundraising stunts.

Indeed, it is not the most usual thing for a nurse to think of Hell's Angels and a local radio DJ serving free ice cream as the highlights of their nursing career. The fun didn't stop there:

"We had a running joke with our long-serving colleague, Meg Cleghorn. If someone asked 'Have you seen Meg?', the nurses would answer with 'asleep on the laundry', or 'sitting on the compost in the garden', referring to one of the hospice's cats Meg! Once in a nurses' meeting, someone asked if Meg was given her de-wormer tablets, and of course we all looked at Meg and asked if she's taken her de-worming tablets!"

Alongside Maria, a band of volunteers played an important part in the day-to-day running of the unit. One of them was Mark West from Luton, who was with the hospice for eight years. Mark did various roles within the charity, from volunteering to administration to care.

Among others, he served as a Day Hospice and bereavement volunteer, personal assistant to the Matron, and senior care administrator. He started as a volunteer in 1993 in the Day Hospice.

There was barely a dull moment during these years for Mark. The most enjoyable ones from the early 1990s were making the patients in Day Hospice feel at home.

"I was the only man in the Day Hospice. At first, a new patient would come in and I remember I would ask 'What drink would you like?' and they would go for a cuppa. They would then see the other patients going for something more serious, and the following day or several days later the patient's cuppa gets swapped for a glass of something even more enjoyable. We tried to make it as comfortable, enjoyable and as homely for everyone as we could."

Mark's background and upbringing (his father was a spiritual leader) meant it was more natural for him to deal with terminal illness and death issues.

"The hospice was a tightly knit team. Everyone knew each other. I honestly cannot remember a moment when I thought 'Oh, I can't do this'. And most of all, it is down to one of the important things about the place – you can always go and talk to somebody. So you would just lean on my colleague, Jeff's door, because he had the office next to mine. You wouldn't necessarily ask for any help, but you would just have a chat. And he would do the same to me and there would be this self-support mechanism where you would just help each other out."

The year of

Change

FINANCE AND GENERAL PURPOSES COMMITTEE

Mr Eric Fountain OBE (Chairman)
Mr Chris Howe BA ACA
Dr David Stegler MD FRCP
Mr Martin Johnson BD M.Mgt (ex Officio)
Mrs Barbara Kettley RGN DN PWT (ex Officio)
Mr Tim Watson LLB

APPEAL COMMITTEE

Mr Jack Sepsworth (Chairman)
Mrs Phyllis Edwards (Secretary)

Mr Paul Armitage
Mr Peter Aspinall
Mr Alan Bartram
Mr Geoffrey Betridge
Miss Julie Bonner

Miss Kathy Leather
Mr John Maddox
Mr John Murtagh
Mr George Pearce
Mr Paul Stevenson

DIRECTORS OF THE TRADING COMPANY

Mr M Johnson BD MIMgt (Chairman)
Mrs Joan Gray (Co Secretary)
Mr John Butterton
Mr Robert Oakley FCA
Mr Michael Snoxell

HONORARY MEDICAL DIRECTOR

Dr David Stegler MD FRCP

MATRON

Mrs Barbara Kettley RGN DN PWT

GENERAL MANAGER

Mr Martin Johnson BD MIMgt

APPEAL MANAGER

Mr Roger Sharp

CHAIRMAN'S MESSAGE

Following three years of consolidation, 1995 has been a year of ebullient activity and of development to respond to the increasing demands upon us from the community who funded the building of the Hospice and who continue to offer us loyal support.

The extension is now nearly complete and we hope to completely move in early in the New Year. We will then be able to double our capacity in Day Care, provide a dedicated teaching facility for the first time, and adequate office space for all members of our multi-disciplinary team, and house the Appeals Department within the Hospice.

Our Home Care nursing team, Hospice Link, has been operational since the Spring and has established an important role as the bridge between the in-patient section of the Hospice and the patients at home, and their professional and family carers.

Once the extension is fully operational, we will be able to offer a regular teaching programme for doctors and nurses and all other professionals involved in all aspects of palliative care, and also for voluntary groups. If we can demonstrate the demand for such teaching, we will then give more serious consideration to a separate teaching, conference and research centre near the Hospice building, the potential need for which we have identified in our strategic plans for the future.

We have reviewed our fundraising organisation and formed a new Appeals Committee under the Chairmanship of Jack Sepsworth, to co-ordinate our many community fundraising activities, and to support the Hospice Appeals Department.

The hospice's yearbook of 1996

The year when the Powdrill Centre opened its doors was also the time when the total annual income for the hospice exceeded £1 million for the first time. The new extension also provided three different rooms for meetings and training events. By spring 1996, they had already been used by a variety of local organisations, including Hospice At Home volunteers, the Motor Neurone Disease Association, Bedfordshire Health Authority, and the Lodge (local HIV/AIDS centre).

The first hospice event to be held in the 2nd floor conference room was the Fifth Anniversary service, which was run by the hospice Chaplains (with help from staff and the Rt Revd David Farmbrough, formerly Bishop of Bedford, and one of the patrons). General Manager, Martin Johnson, said:

"It was a welcome change to be able to set up and host such an event without the massive disruption to day care and other hospice activities. In a year when we've coped with many changes, especially with all the problems of the building work, and yet helped more patients than ever in one way or another, all I can say is 'Well done everybody!'"

Many at the hospice then agreed that the year in the run up to the Day Hospice opening was 'The Year of Change'. The vision of delivering a service that was 'needs-led' was becoming a reality. Matron, Barbara Kettley, then said:

"Our community's needs are paramount and the improvements in the service we can provide will be more and better day care and the introduction of our Home Care Service, 'Hospice Link', thereby trebling the number of patients we care for."

From Strength To Strength

> ❝ It is clear from the local community support and from the many letters which are received that the hospice is very dear to the hearts of many people. ❞

During this time, fundraising kept growing from strength to strength. Appeals manager Roger Sharp noted:

> *"It is clear from the local community support and from the many letters which are received that the hospice is very dear to the hearts of many people".*

In a bid to boost good relationships with local businesses, the hospice became a member of Bedfordshire Chamber of Commerce. The year also saw an introduction of a new Appeals Committee chaired by Jack Sapsworth, a member of the Council of Management. It was proving to be hugely successful. Richard Field became the chairman of the Community Fundraising Committee with the aim to set up support groups throughout the hospice's catchment area. The annual summer fête, which started in 1994, moved to a new venue at Barnfield College, which proved to be ideal, raising over £11,000 that summer.

As well as helping with the relentless task of fundraising, volunteers at this time were contributing to all areas of service within and outside the hospice, all equally important to the whole. Earlier that year, on the annual volunteer social evening, the trustees of the hospice were proud to present long service awards to volunteers who have served the hospice for 5 years or longer. Matron Barbara Kettley admitted:

> *"It was a very special and memorable occasion, and it is wonderful to see the special 5 year badges being worn by our volunteers with great pride."*

Roger Sharp fundraising era: profile in the local newspaper

“It was a very *Special* and memorable occasion, and it is wonderful to see the special 5 year badges being worn by our volunteers with great *Pride*”

Now and then:

The Keech Palliative Care Centre in 2011

The most recent refurbishment to the Day Hospice has come a long way since the Powdrill Centre was opened in 1996. The newly named Keech Palliative Care Centre (KPCC) reopened in May 2011. Thanks to a grant from the Department of Health, the KPCC now offered a light and spacious environment with a range of sitting and activity areas, including a dedicated art room and pool and football tables.

Speaking about the latest development, Adult Services Manager, *Elaine Tolliday,* said at the opening:

"The service...

offers an individual and flexible service to adult patients with a life threatening illness whose symptoms or emotional needs require support. As people live longer with cancer and other life threatening illnesses more now than ever before it is vital that our services are there and available when people need them.

"On referral, we meet with the patient and offer an assessment which includes the setting of goals that the patient wishes to achieve. These may be things like being pain free so they can go out with family for lunch or having the confidence to go shopping. The initial programme of care can include full days, part days or drop-in sessions. Patients are offered the opportunity to choose which suits their lifestyle best. For example if they are working, a drop-in is best for them."

Moving forward: the refurbishments in 2011

Patients can then access all the services including time with doctors and nurses, support from the specialist social worker, complementary therapies, music therapy, use of the hydrotherapy pool, and counselling. The palliative care centre also offers blood transfusions and intravenous fluids so the patients don t have to go to hospital. Elaine said:

"After the first 6 weeks we meet with the patient to see how things are going. We can then alter their care as things change. Patients are then offered a further 6 weeks of care. Only when and if the patient and health care professional feel they have achieved the goals originally set does the patient stop coming regularly. They are always welcome to drop-in and the hospice is always there in the background.

"For carers we offer a support group that runs every Monday afternoon and every third Monday evening of the month. Carers are also offered one-to-one sessions as required."

Twenty one years on, the Palliative Care Centre is offering this individual and flexible service to more patients than ever before.

"As a driver, I felt like a part of the patients' therapy. I wasn't just getting them from their home to the hospice - we had lots of conversations."

Tales of the Road

A volunteer's story

An advert about the Open Day at the newly built hospice in 1990 led to 20 years of dedication from a handful of original volunteers. If there is a way to describe the dedication spanning through more than two decades by selfless giving of one's skills, time and care, it is through the eyes of these longest serving volunteers at the hospice.

A retired home economics teacher and a born and bred Lutonian, **Mary Moatt**, 73, remembers taking along her friend when she decided to attend one of the first Open Days in the freshly built hospice. Mary was one of the many, who came on board after hearing the new hospice's urgent public plea for manpower. The concept of a hospice was not new to Mary, as she had already seen a TV programme about the hospices, felt impressed and had warmed to the idea. It was just before Easter 1990 and her first impression was one of a very welcoming, comfortable and new home away from home, ready and finished for those who need it. The tour around the new hospice, made Mary remember both her parents that had suffered from cancer and how pleased they would be to see a place like that. She signed up on the spot and marked driving as her preferred volunteering option. After an interview with Faith Tournay, Volunteer Coordinator at the time, Mary came in one Thursday in June for her first once-a-week shift as a Day Hospice driver. The volunteer driver would collect the Day Centre patients and occasionally their visitors in the morning from their home and drive them back in the late afternoon.

There were many memorable patients for Mary, too many to mention them all. Among countless inevitable sad moments, Mary remembers a few amusing ones too. The 'difficult customers', like a man who hated being driven by anyone else, least of all a woman or the bossy lady who was used to ordering everyone about. These were just a few that Mary had to deal with. Finding a common ground was Mary's tactic with the 'difficult customers'; easing the minutes spent in the car by chatting away about family trees, holidays, war time memories – anything that interested the patients and made them warm up and mellow towards their driver over time.

There was an Irish patient, who would greet his driver with a cheerful and loud "Oh, hello, Mary!" and in the short journey to the Day Hospice would manage to tell her in detail about his recent holiday in Ireland. There was a lady, who used to serve in a huge mansion when she was young and shared her memories, always a treat for Mary.

"As a driver, I felt like a part of the patients' therapy. I wasn't just getting them from their home to the hospice – we had lots of conversations. Throughout my twenty years, most of the first-time patients would tell me in the car: 'I don't think I should be going'. Feeling how apprehensive and uneasy they felt, I tried my best to encourage them, and make them feel relaxed as I drove. When time came to collect them in the afternoon, I could hear a sense of relief and surprise in their voice. 'It was wonderful,' they would tell me on the way back."

"When they relaxed I found myself often hearing things about their everyday life and their condition, which I used to report to nurses. It was a part of my job to listen and make them feel at ease."

Mary's two decades of driving the hospice patients means more than 8,000 hours given away to the cause that grew very close to Mary's heart. However, these staggering numbers tell only half of the story.

From
roads to loafs

Eight years ago Mary felt she could be doing more for her hospice. Her background as a home economics teacher and her abundant homemade jam supplies replenished every summer made her think about a stall selling cakes at the "Crafts for Christmas" event at Barnfield College in Luton. Every year she rallies her friends at their local Church Of The Holy Family to make and bring cakes to sell at the stall in late October, where every last cake gets sold and Mary's sales reach up to £600.

The preparation starts early: Mary is keen to make as much jam as the season harvest allows, thoroughly plan each day's baking batches of the week before the event, stock up on donated supplies, recruit cake decorators and arrange help for that all important Saturday. Mary thinks through the cake decor, the freshness, the logistics, the packaging – all is well prepared before the big event.

"I told the fundraiser, Mark Relf, last year that I would eat my hat, if I didn't make £500 on the day, judging from the volume of cakes we'd baked. Thinking I was wearing a Lutonian straw hat that day, it would have been quite a tall order! Thankfully, we did a great job selling all the cakes and made £650, which was all profit, a lovely £200 increase from last year."

Mary is all set to bake her cakes for another 'Crafts for Christmas'. Only, she admits, it will be a less grand a stand this time round as Mary is fighting cancer, diagnosed in February 2011. Having faced many cancer patients in her two decades with the hospice, the experience has helped Mary to take the illness in her stride.

> *"When I went to the hospital for an operation, I made everything a part of my "I Want to Get Better Campaign". I took with me a picture of a Protea flower that I took in Tasmania to keep in the ward, which reminded me I have to get fit quickly and get back to travelling.*
>
> *I also followed the advice of my friend who's gone through cancer herself and brought along a bright pink pillowcase with me. You see, the hospital's white bed linen doesn't flatter one's pale complexion, to put it subtly."*

Mary's 20 years of volunteering badge that she received in September 2011 is not the only epitome of her devotion to the hospice cause: Mary is determined to get back to driving. With Mary's natural determination and drive, there is no room for doubt.

"The *experience* has helped *Mary* to take the illness in her stride."

Chapter Eight

What's in a name?

THE PASQUE ADULT HOSPICE

LUTON AND SOUTH BEDS · HOSPICE

"It was agreed that this was a name which would take the charity forward while enabling it to continue using the unique emblem of the Pasque flower."

In the years before the adult hospice first opened, the name it should take was debated a number of times. The building was called Betty Robinson House, after the lady who had bestowed the land, but the name 'Luton and South Bedfordshire Hospice' was chosen for the charity itself with the wild Pasque flower adopted as its emblem.

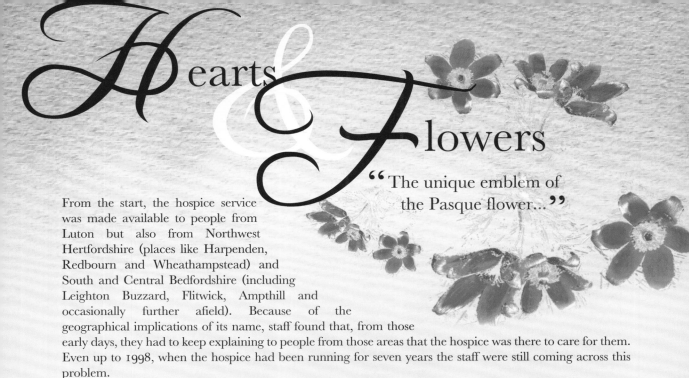

Hearts & Flowers

> "The unique emblem of the Pasque flower..."

From the start, the hospice service was made available to people from Luton but also from Northwest Hertfordshire (places like Harpenden, Redbourn and Wheathampstead) and South and Central Bedfordshire (including Leighton Buzzard, Flitwick, Ampthill and occasionally further afield). Because of the geographical implications of its name, staff found that, from those early days, they had to keep explaining to people from those areas that the hospice was there to care for them. Even up to 1998, when the hospice had been running for seven years the staff were still coming across this problem.

1998 proved to be the year for coming up with new names. With the children's hospice project underway, trustees were already looking for a name for this new side of the charity and decided it was time to rename the adult service too. The Board of Trustees, management team and staff were all involved in the discussions that took place about the name and many different ideas were put forward. When the name 'Pasque Hospice' was canvassed to hospice supporters, staff and volunteers, it was agreed that this was a name which would take the charity forward while enabling it to continue using the unique emblem of the Pasque flower. Medical Director at the time, Dr Elizabeth Horak commented in 1998:

> *"To mark this new stage of our development we will take on a new name. A name which refers to our original emblem – the Pasque flower. As the Pasque flower is native to this area, Pasque Hospice hopes to be part of the community's life. Pasque Hospice is happy to assume the identity and name from this cherished little flower, associated with spring, with the mystery of Easter and with the peace of local woodlands."*

When it came to addressing a name for the children's hospice, consideration had to be given to two things: firstly that the service would be caring for children from a much wider geographical area than its adult counterpart; and secondly that it would need to function as part of the existing charity. In due course, the name 'Keech Cottage' was chosen, in honour of Dennis and Shirley Keech, whose donation of £1 million began the children's hospice appeal in April 1998. The name was branded with a logo of its own, a house with a heart. At the time, the Board hoped that the name and its insignia would invoke a homely feeling, making it easier for families to accept hospice care for their child and helping them to overcome the idea that a hospice is somewhere people go to die. Keech Cottage wanted its patients, families and supporters to see that it was a place where children could have fun and meet new friends; a place for the whole family to get the care and support they need; and a safe and comforting place for families to leave their child while taking a deserved break from their 24-hour care routine.

Following the opening of the children's service in 2000, the two hospice services worked in unison and under a streamlined management structure. In 2002 it was decided that, while retaining the names Pasque Hospice and Keech Cottage, the organisation would also use an umbrella name to embrace all its work, The Pasque Charity.

"Pasque Hospice is *Happy* to assume the identity and name from this *Cherished* little flower, associated with spring, with the mystery of Easter and with the peace of the local woodlands."

The Pasque Charity
working on behalf of

(Left) Pasque charity logo,
(Right) Keech Cottage logo,

Three names for one organisation

While the organisation continued to grow and develop over the next few years, the charity came to see the use of three different names to describe two hospice services as problematic. 'The Pasque Charity' name conveyed nothing about the actual work of the charity and was rarely able to be used without further explanation. The two hospice names and logos shared nothing to link them together as one organisation and 'Keech Cottage' was especially limited in implying a building based service, whereas much of the charity's work was actually conducted in the community. On top of this, there were significant costs associated with the design and print of various literature using the different names and logos. All of this meant there were considerable difficulties in the day-to-day running of the charity and confusion among patients, their families and the charity's supporters. Chief Executive in 2009, David White, explained further:

"In many ways, it would have been easy for us to write off some of these problems as inconveniences and live with them in favour of maintaining the status quo. However, we believe that having one simplified identity will help to overcome these issues and help patients and supporters to have a better understanding of the work we do locally to improve people's lives."

At its combined public meeting and volunteer evening on 30th September 2009, the charity announced its new single identity, 'Keech Hospice Care'. Communications Manager, Nicola Field, unveiled the name and its corresponding logo to the 200 strong audience who, judging by the spontaneous applause which broke out after her presentation, received the new name with enthusiasm! Nicola commented:

"The round of applause was quite unexpected but happily received. To prepare for the new identity, so much had needed to be re-written and re-designed – everything from new letter headed paper to an entire new website. This had involved months of hard work from the Communications team and it was so nice to get such an encouraging response. After the unveiling, I remember breathing a sigh of relief as many of the audience came to personally share their positive comments on the new name and branding."

The new name went live the very next day and would, from then onwards, encompass every aspect of the charity's work – children, adults, in-house and community.

Prior to its launch, the charity had conducted months of research involving staff, volunteers, trustees, patients, families and the public. As part of this, Keech had sent out a survey to residents across the organisation's catchment area, the aim being to give a clear idea of what the public knew about the charity, its work, its values and the existing names.

The results highlighted a number of insights; firstly that 'Keech' was the name most people recognised; secondly that that the word 'hospice' was an important description of the charity's services; and thirdly that 'care' was seen as its core value. Combining these strongest elements of the charity's branding produced the name 'Keech Hospice Care'.

The new name was accompanied by a new logo, designed in-house by James Lomas, a member of the Communications team at that time. Featuring two interlinking hearts, representative of the two hospices working together, the logo also retained a sense of history by comprising the two colours that the charity had been using for some time – purple for the adult hospice and blue for the children's service.

Despite the change of logo, the Pasque flower is an emblem which remained dear to many of the charity's supporters and because of that, Keech made efforts to ensure it retained some of its special significance at the organisation. Visit the hospice today and you'll still find traces of the Pasque flower around the building and gardens – engraved into a stone close to the entrance, imprinted on towels and appearing as a design feature on the windows of the adult In-patient Unit. You may even find one or two within the pages of this book.

Knowing there would be some local sensitivity about the change of name, the charity was focused on ensuring everyone was well informed as to the reasons behind it and that it changed nothing about the charity's work, values and dedication to the local community. Supporters, staff and volunteers received newsletters explaining more about the new branding and the charity engaged with several members of the local media to get a significant amount of coverage for the news. Chief Executive today, Mike Keel commented on the charity's evolving name:

"As the scope of our work has developed over the years, so too has the need to bring greater clarity within our branding. The move to 'Keech Hospice Care' has greatly helped us achieve this and we are sure it will effectively take us through all the developments, challenges and growth we face in the years ahead – during our 21st birthday year and far beyond."

"I Remember

breathing a sigh of relief as many of the audience came to personally share their positive comments on the new name and branding."

Keech Hospice Care logo

The Luton News reporting on the new branding at Keech, Oct 2009

The Pasque Flower

The Pasque flower is one of the most beautiful wild flowers to be found within South Bedfordshire. It is a small anemone like flower with a delicate purple hue to its petals. The name Pasque means Easter, the time of year when the blooms can be seen and it is also known as the resurrection flower. On the exposed chalk downs, close to the hospice, the beautiful flowers bravely bloom on hostile windswept hillsides. The Pasque flower, like the hospice, is a symbol of hope and renewal. Wink White remembers how it came to be adopted as the emblem of the hospice:

"We knew that the name Luton and South Bedfordshire Hospice was not popular among our Dunstable supporters. Then, one day, Iris and I were walking on the Chiltern Hills at Barton when we came across the lovely purple anemone struggling for light through the grass. Our trustees and supporters immediately adopted the Pasque flower as our logo and name of the hospice – the most unique and lovely logo in the hospice world. As our supporters and friends said, the little flower is an emblem of peace, resurrection and courage."

"Everyone at the hospice was there for us, picking up the pieces and helping us begin the process of dealing with life without our loved one."

A personal recollection of hospice care

Having always known the Pasque Hospice, as it was then, it wasn't until I was working for Dennis Keech and through his enormous generosity that enabled the children's hospice to be born, that I became aware of just "what goes on" at a hospice. It's truly amazing. I can't begin to express the immense gratitude that my family alone have to everyone involved at Keech.

It was July 1999 that my eldest brother, Douglas, was cared for here so gently and with so much attention to dignity during his fight against cancer. One year later, his wife was given the exact same treatment when she too lost her battle with cancer. Our beloved daughter, Linda, came to Keech in January 2005. She had battled ovarian cancer for almost four years. Her pain was excruciating but the nurses had it under control within the hour of her arriving. Linda

didn't want to go to the hospice, to her it was a place to die and she firmly believed she could beat this disease. I remember on the journey from Mount Vernon she said she wasn't sure she'd made the right choice. I told her to trust me, I wouldn't let her go somewhere that I wasn't 100% happy with.

After settling her in her room a nurse arrived with a beautifully set tray – white doily, china cups and saucers, pot of tea, pot of coffee, and a wonderful selection of scrummy home-made cakes. On the corner of the tray was a vase with a beautiful red carnation. My daughter looked at me, gave me a huge smile and said, "Mum, I think I'm going to like it here after all".

That prayer had been answered. Linda was 44, but to herself and us she was still 20. She was fun, kind to all, loved everyone and organised so many things. She especially had fun times, despite being so ill, with nurses Kim, Sally and Mark, who she teased relentlessly. Even Dr Judith Summers was persuaded to bring in her rather large dog to say "hello".

What followed was hilarious. I won't try to describe the scene as I could be in deep trouble here!! But it only went to show that "here" nothing was impossible. Sadly when Linda passed away we were all devastated and filled with grief, but everyone at the hospice was there for us, picking up the pieces and helping us begin the process of dealing with life without our loved one. Alas in 2009 my best friend, Eileen Sharp, needed the aid of the hospice. Her only son lives in the USA. When he came over when his mum was so ill, I'm so glad that I was able to point him in the right direction to get the help that Eileen so badly needed. He too was totally amazed by this amazing place. Finally, I would just like to mention the importance to us all of The Lights of Love service and the thanksgiving services that are held. Not only do they bring us all together to reflect and remember our loved ones, but also to remember and give thanks to all at the hospice who are still there for any of us whenever we feel the need to make contact for whatever reason.

Thank you Keech – you're wonderful.

Daphne & David Hill

Chapter Nine

'A short life deserves a special kind of care'

"Betty Robinson, who had already done so much, kindly gave two acres of land to the west of the main buildings as the preferred site."

Caring for a child with a life limiting condition puts an incredible strain on family life. A full night's sleep and normal mealtimes become impossible; holidays and outings are rare. Healthy brothers and sisters inevitably feel left out as the attention focuses on the sick child. Parents may have to give up work to care for their child 24 hours a day and many must learn to perform difficult nursing procedures.

The charity designed Keech Cottage to be a place where families can come and stay in times of crisis or when they need a rest. Over the months or years that the hospice supports a child and family, staff form a special bond with them built on trust and an understanding of their personal circumstances.

Planning for the children's hospice began shortly after the adult Day Hospice and out-patient unit was opened in January 1996. John Maddox DL (Deputy Lieutenant), a hospice trustee at the time who became involved with the Luton and South Beds Hospice in 1995 through his membership of Luton Rotary Club, was already knowledgeable in fundraising matters. John remembers:

"Back in the Boardroom the ink from the Powdrill Centre negotiations was hardly dry before the idea of a children's hospice to sit alongside the adult complex became a serious topic of conversation and research. Martin Johnson, the General Manager, had been sponsored to take a three year degree course at The University of Bedfordshire and would go on to write his thesis about the national hospice movement, its staggering growth in recent years, and where it was going in the future. This guiding document and an increasing awareness of the need in our area drove trustees to decide that a children's hospice for Bedfordshire and Hertfordshire was vital and that, if built on the existing site, economies of scale in administration could be achieved. With only two dozen children's hospices in the country at the time and only three built on adult sites a degree of pioneering spirit would be required as well as a mere 2 million pounds.

"Companion of the hospice, Betty Robinson, who had already done so much, kindly gave two acres of land to the West of the main buildings as the preferred site. The outline plans submitted for approval were for a square building with a garden in the middle built around the oak tree on the donated land. The original idea was to keep the buildings close but completely separate. After much official debate and some public protest, South Bedfordshire Councillors rejected the location and insisted the children's unit was brought much closer to the adult unit so there was less encroachment into 'Green Belt Land'. Generously, Betty gave another two acres South of Day Care and gifted all land to the Board. This allowed the building to be positioned close to the adult unit and, after several revisions, the building now included a hydrotherapy pool and an educational/conference facility. By November 1997, the Council had passed the plans, subject to the Secretary of State giving his approval and there being no objections to the public footpath, diverted from a route through the proposed building, to around the boundaries of the existing hospice.

"I well recall the excitement in the Boardroom when senior Trustee, Eric Fountain, confided that another benefactor had pledged 1 million pounds. After much discussion with this benefactor, he and his family reluctantly agreed to lend their name to the project which became known as Keech Cottage Children's Hospice. The project was gathering momentum now and another fundraiser was required to concentrate on this special appeal. Mrs Carol Bagni was appointed.

"Carol's energy and enthusiasm soon attracted supporters from all areas. One such offer was from the Irish community, led by long-term supporter Don Wall of South Beds Golf Club, who agreed to prepare the site for the new building by levelling it with their excavation equipment and create a huge bank along the perimeter to protect the children's garden from the fierce winds that can blow over the Chilterns. They did this over one weekend free of charge and saved the charity thousands of pounds."

One of Carol's first tasks was to officially launch the children's hospice appeal on April 30th 1998, with a £3 million target to build Keech Cottage next to the adult hospice. The new hospice was to serve the areas of Bedfordshire and Hertfordshire at first; the charity decided on this plan from the results of a needs assessment and consultation with health authorities and professionals throughout Bedfordshire and Hertfordshire in 1997. This research estimated there were around 300 children in the proposed catchment area, who doctors had diagnosed as having life-limiting conditions. Mr Dennis Keech, gave £1 million towards the appeal – £500,000 on the launch date and the remaining £500,000 to be matched with other donations as an incentive for the appeal. This worked and Keech soon had £1.5m. After three years of fundraising, campaigning and building works, the charity proudly opened its new children's hospice, Keech Cottage, on 28th March 2000.

Betty Robinson offered the land to build Keech Cottage. Betty at the moving the top soil ceremony with Dr Siegler left, and The Lord Lieutenant of Bedfordshire

Keech Cottage appeal fundraising efforts

Backing the vision

When talks about a new children's hospice began, the management team were determined to make sure that families, professionals and the community saw it as a specialist clinical service. Martin Johnson, General Manager at the time, commented:

"We were well aware there were children's hospices that were regarded as little more than cuddly nursing homes. We did not want to project that image. So, from the beginning we put in place a clinical team who wanted to innovate."

Between April 1998 and September 1999, the Keech family donation was added to the further £2 million raised from the public by every means imaginable. There were balls, sponsored cycle rides, marathon runners and parachute jumpers. Groups of Brownies, Cubs, Scouts, Guides, Air Cadets, Army Cadets, school children of all ages and every other youth and children's organisation you can think of took part. And there were the personal donations, from a few pounds up to the tens of thousands, coming in by the hundred, month after month. The hospice's community fundraiser at the time, Roger Sharp, said:

1.75m appeal for children's hospice

Barbara Kettley in the local news in 1997

"... Our vision is to provide ongoing support for families facing the loss of their child. But, dreams can remain dreams, without the financial support of people committed to making dreams come true."

John Maddox remembered the publicity and media support that the progressing appeal enjoyed:

"From 1998 to 2000 the coverage in local newspapers of what was proposed was intense and Three Counties Radio joined in when regular presenter, BBC's Jon Gaunt, frequently mentioned the project on air. John was known for being forthright and opinionated on his morning show – regularly taking on local officials and challenging them. His reaction was not surprising when it was reported that vandals had got onto the building site in the middle of the night and smashed most of the newly delivered double glazed windows waiting on pallets to be installed. He was incensed."

Martin Johnson recalls:

"It shocked the building team. I arrived that morning to find this big burly site foreman almost in tears. He just couldn't believe people would do such a thing. I decided we needed to go public with this and the story went out on local news that day. Before long, donations had poured in and there was enough to get the windows replaced. It was heart-warming to see such support and it was a real case of turning bad into good."

"... I arrived that morning to find this big burly site foreman almost in tears."

The local press were quick to publicise the act of vandalism. The Luton News wrote on the incident:

"The vandals hurled bricks, lumps of concrete and other missiles at windows and doors, smashing glass and seriously damaging the aluminium outer frames. Pasque Hospice staff and the T & E Neville construction team were devastated to discover the damage at the hospice site on Tuesday morning and now hope the attack will not delay completion of the building."

Jon Gaunt raged against the mindless vandals on his Breakfast Show and this rallied the community to help remedy the situation. He even had the internal children's garden named 'Gaunty's Garden' after he arranged for it to be landscaped following an appeal on the radio. A presentation to the wider world at Vauxhall's Riverside Centre was also a success where Trustee, Jo Wrighton played a major role, but the team were having great difficulty getting the message beyond Luton and South Bedfordshire. John Maddox remembered:

"Our second lottery, designed for a wider audience in Bedfordshire and Hertfordshire was having some impact and, I recall, Carol excitedly telling the Board how the Stevenage newspapers were running a major campaign. This breakthrough into new communities was encouraging and you could feel a new sense of enthusiasm in everyone involved."

One notable and innovative fundraising event was an idea dreamt up by Carol Bagni. With an airport close to us she wanted to challenge the airlines to fly a butterfly around the world. The butterfly was chosen because it is the emblem of the UK children's hospice movement and accurately reflects the short but precious lives of the children Keech planned to serve. The airlines loved the idea and soon it was taking shape. One problem to overcome was how the 'butterfly' would be transported. Airline and customs restrictions really challenged Carol but with her artistic background she soon solved the problem by making a silk butterfly that could be put into a sturdy cardboard tube for transit but easily revealed for press and photographic opportunities. It was the baton the airlines would pass between each other.

With much pomp and ceremony the butterfly set off on its journey on 16th September 1998 and travelled from Heathrow to Gatwick via Frankfurt, Bangkok, Sydney, Honolulu and Houston. It was endorsed by Luton airport based airlines and raised money through people sponsoring the various legs of its journey. In its first year the butterfly's journey raised £4,500 towards the appeal and was flying around the world with even more sponsors once again a year later in 1999. During its journey, the hospice received updates on where in the world it had got to and which airline was looking after it at any one time. All seemed to be going smoothly until it was realised that the butterfly would arrive back in the UK at Gatwick and not Luton! Ever resourceful, and through a contact at the GMB union at Luton Airport, Carol put in a call to the only person known to have his own fleet of aircraft at the airport, Mr Mohammed Al Fayed.

He readily agreed to put his helicopter at the charity's disposal to bring the butterfly back from Gatwick to Luton, where it would be welcomed back at a children's party arranged for the families who had been helping to plan the hospice in a newly built (but not yet opened) part of the terminal. At the last minute, Carol discovered Mr Al Fayed himself was going to bring the butterfly to the party and would bring presents for the children and families from his store – Harrods. This level of local support helped convince the National Lottery Charities Board and other major funding trusts that they too should back this project with £500,000.

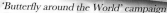

'Butterfly around the World' campaign

Hiccups
along the way

Away from the fundraising, John Maddox remembers more turbulence along the way:

"We recruited Mike Keel in 1998 for his expertise to help design and open the children's hospice. He decided straight away that he would bring together a group of families he had known from his time at the Cambridge Children's Hospice to help advise him on the new service. This meant the end result was a much better building than first planned (even though the team had already taken the best advice of several existing children's hospices).

However, these changes and rising building costs resulted in the anticipated costs growing. The group recommended things like a room for siblings; a hydrotherapy pool (essential for the children – most of whom have severe disabilities and benefit from therapeutic swimming); office space for the newly created community nursing team; and an area for running training courses to teach others about children's palliative care. The families also 'invented' the uniform for the nurses and carers. Children's hospices had avoided uniforms for staff to keep a more homely feel but the family group revealed that they found it hard to distinguish between trained nurses, carers and other parents when everyone wore their ordinary clothes. They came up with an informal uniform of polo shirts and this has now been adopted by most of the other UK children's hospices.

"Keech has led the way in many of its services and procedures. These improvements to the design of the building inevitably meant the costs went up but the trustees and staff were determined that the new building should be of high-quality (so it lasts); low maintenance and efficient (to keep running costs down) and fit for purpose without compromise on what the children and families would need. This challenged the architects, Derek Hewitt and Michael Dale, who continually scanned the plans, specifications and design to ensure everything was being done to keep costs under control.

"The fundraisers also had to raise the money for running the hospice in its first year as well as the building costs, unfortunately the press and others only focussed on the building costs. Good news in the summer of 1999 was a record breaking weekend at the Midsummer Show when over 5000 people attended and clear profit hit £18,000. This had been preceded by the Luton Carnival where the fundraising team manned and dressed a 50ft trailer to resemble the building site ongoing at Great Bramingham Lane."

Despite all the challenges, the appeal was gaining speed and the target of opening Keech Cottage in 2000 was looking more than promising.

Assembling the team and appeal in full speed

The building was only a part of the story, however. Even before the plans had been completed, Mike Keel had decided the service should begin as soon as possible and before the building was complete. He applied to the BBC Children in Need fund and was delighted to receive the full amount of his application and set about recruiting five nurses to form the Pasque Community Team – the first dedicated children's hospice community team in the UK.

The team had three priorities: to start finding the families who would use the hospice and start giving them information and support at home for those who needed it; to start publicising the new hospice to professionals in the health and social services so the service could be fully integrated and families would be told about it; and finally to be the face of the appeal throughout the two counties, helping to raise money and awareness in the community. The team began work in September 1998, and by the beginning of the 2000, had worked with over 60 children and their

Mohammed Al Fayed's support in the local news

families. During 1999, already 10 of their child patients had died, proving beyond doubt the need of the service, and also increasing the sense of urgency in getting Keech Cottage ready for full operation.

While the planning of the building had been going on, there had also been a lot of behind-the-scenes work on considering how the service will work, and discussions had been taking place with professionals from the Health Service and Social Services in Bedfordshire and Hertfordshire, and with various voluntary organisations with a part to play. On 5th December 1998 the Keech Cottage appeal reached an amazing £2m. Raising so much, so quickly, showed the extraordinary support the Appeal had received from the local community. Even before the New Year dawned, the appeal had just £800,000 to go to reach the £3m target. An enormous figure admittedly, but one that Director of Fundraising at the time, Carol Bagni, was confident the appeal could reach:

"Our supporters have worked so hard already. Raising £2m is an enormous achievement. Now I hope we all try twice as hard to reach £3m. I'm sure we can do it!"

Anyone visiting the hospice that winter would notice construction of Keech Cottage was well under way. The winter saw its foundations finished, the walls beginning to appear and the hydrotherapy pool taking shape. The fundraising drive to complete Keech Cottage was to continue to get the maximum publicity, but maintaining the existing hospice service for adults and the commitment to improving

it were also important. General Manager Martin Johnson said:

"The hospice service of care is very much like a proverbial iceberg – 80% of it is 'out of site'. The In-patient Unit provides the very visible and important 20% of our service to those patients who really need the high levels of care that can only be provided in this facility, but the less visible work of the Day Hospice has seen the most dramatic increase in care, both in numbers and quality. Then, almost completely out of site, is the work we do with all our professional colleagues in the community."

Hitting the target

It began on the 30th April 1998 with a £1m donation from Dennis Keech. It ended on the 6th October 1999 with a grant of over £500,000 from the National Lottery Charities Board. In the intervening 18 months, a huge community fundraising effort had driven the Keech Cottage Capital Appeal to its final £3 million target just as the roof to the new building was complete. Carol Bagni, who oversaw the community effort as Director of Fundraising, said:

"It's absolutely fantastic. To have reached the target in such a short time is, we believe, a regional fundraising record and it's all down to the local community. We cannot thank them enough!"

Early stages of the construction work

104

"It's absolutely fantastic. To have reached the target in such a short time is, we believe, a regional fundraising record and it's all down to the local community. We cannot thank them enough!"

Dennis Keech was the main benefactor of Keech Cottage

The race to raise the £3 million target saw people taking part in everything from sponsored parachute jumps, to pancake races, to aeroplane walks and sponsored head shaves. Then there were all the charity auctions, concerts, golf days and garden parties organised on behalf of Keech Cottage throughout Bedfordshire and Hertfordshire.

To finish the job

Over the spring and summer months of 1999, construction of Keech Cottage had progressed rapidly and in September it was already possible to see how the new children's hospice would look. Martin Johnson said at the time:

"I think everyone who sees the building feels a sense of pride in what the community is accomplishing. The whole setting will be very beautiful and there are some stunning views both from Keech Cottage itself and the hill behind it. The feeling that a number of people have shared with me is the difference between how nice the place will be and how tragic are the situations of those people who need to come here. My answer is that we can only give our best and do our best to help.

"We are already caring for the children and their families, even though we do not yet have a hospice for them. At the last count, the Pasque Community Nurses are working with over 40 families and making a big difference in their lives. Once the building is finished, we estimate that a full package of care will cost about £5,800 per year for each family supported."

John Maddox recalled the atmosphere of anticipation once the building was nearly ready:

"In the run up to the opening year 2000 rumours were spreading of general fundraising fatigue and interest from Trusts and Foundations waning. Still, the news that a Royal visitor might come to officially open the facilities six months before we would be fully operational was too much for the Board and the offer was accepted with all the extra work that would involve. Liaising with the Lord Lieutenant of Bedfordshire was only the start and it took the inside knowledge of Eric Fountain DL OBE, Chairman of Keech Cottage Appeal, and Chairman of the Board, David Seigler to coordinate the lengthy invitation list, rearrange the timing of a pre-planned flower show inside the new building, select a specimen oak tree for planting and nominate local schools and volunteers whilst allowing as many public to be present as possible.

"An exceptional degree of cooperation was called for in the last few weeks by all concerned but none more so than with the contractors and suppliers of fittings who all removed their various work arrangements whilst a volunteer team of flower arrangers prepared a most wonderful exhibition throughout the entire new complex. Led by Lyn and Jack Sapsworth and ladies of The Chiltern Floral society the uncarpeted, curtainless facilities were transformed throughout to accommodate over two thousand visitors to view what was now their own community children's hospice. Great media coverage once more and a terrific morale boost for all the staff and volunteers."

The new children's hospice for Bedfordshire and Hertfordshire was to have its grand opening on March 28th 2000 with the Princess Royal, but there was still a long way to go on the fundraising side. To run the Keech Cottage in its first year, £900,000 was needed, all of which was to be raised through charitable donations, in addition to £1.1 million needed to maintain the essential adult services in Betty Robinson House. Martin Johnson summed up:

"It's a huge amount, but we are confident we can do it. The people of Bedfordshire and Hertfordshire have supported us this far, we hope they'll continue to do so."

Later stages of the Keech Cottage
construction works

"The feeling...

that a number of people have shared with me is the difference betwen how nice the place will be and how tragic are the situations of those people who need to come here, My answer is that we can only give our best and do our best to help."

Finally there: Keech Cottage building close to completion

The flower festival in the local news

TEATIME: Five-year-old Luke Titmus and teddy enjoy a picnic among the flowers.

Children's hospice makes floral debut

THE impressive facilities at Keech Cottage children's hospice were seen by members of the public for the first time at the weekend.

A flower festival, with exhibits by florists across Beds and Herts, was staged in the building

that is to be opened by the Princess Royal on March 29. Nurses were on hand to tell visitors what each room would be used for. Facilities include family bedrooms, soft play and wet play areas, an all denominational chapel, outdoor playground and a multi-sensory room, complete with fibre-optic wall displays, a water bed and whale music.

Childhood was the theme of the flower festival. Memories captured included days at the seaside, a teddy bears' picnic and all the fun of the fair.

Proceeds from the event – more than £5,000 – will go to the children's hospice's Revenue Appeal. More than £50,000 is needed annually to cover running costs.

Gazetta/News
1/3/

SCENT: Care team worker Val Rees.

SEASIDE THEME: Director of nursing Mike Keel.

TEATIME: Five-year-old Luke Titmus and teddy enjoy a picnic among the flowers.

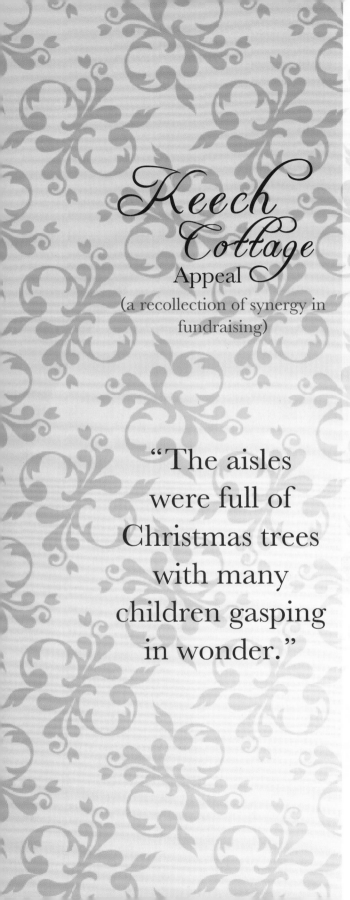

Keech Cottage Appeal

(a recollection of synergy in fundraising)

"The aisles were full of Christmas trees with many children gasping in wonder."

Looking back at my time with Keech, it's difficult to single out one event above another, as so many people did so many wonderful things, especially during the Keech Cottage appeal.

One appeal that stands out for its financial success was the BBC Three Counties Radio on-air appeal in aid of Keech Cottage. Nick Laurence, one of the presenters, came to me proposing such an appeal and we agreed but then the announcement went ahead before they had let us know! Needless to say our phone line was besieged!

With a volunteer force of around 470 I felt pretty sure we had the man/woman power to man phones throughout the day. I approached NTL about them letting us use one of their offices with six phone extensions. The wonderful volunteers organised a rota for manning the phones in four shifts a day for a week, from 6am until 6pm. They were able to take the donors' details and talk to them about Gift Aid. After presenting this plan to Nick, they flagged the appeal up on air for a week preceding the appeal. This was an example of synergy, where several strings are brought together for the common good.

Another example of synergy came one time when a week before Christmas I received a call from a vicar in a Mid Bedfordshire village asking that I attend his Christmas Tree Festival on 23rd December to switch on the lights. I was already booked for two other events that night, one in South Hertfordshire and one in North Bedfordshire. When I explained this, he replied "We are raising money for you, don't you care?". So, I rang the other events and rearranged their times. Subsequently, rushing around the two counties like Santa, I was glad I did. The Festival was amazing. The aisles were full of Christmas trees with many children gasping in wonder.

Back at work in the New Year, I proposed to Canon Nick Bell the idea of replicating this in his much bigger church, The Parish Church of St Mary's in Luton. Eventually we got the go ahead and working together with the church staff, their and our volunteers (one of whom fortunately was an IT buff), we were able to mount a bigger event with the trees lighting sequentially from the rear all the way up to the altar. The trees were sponsored and supporters donated a light to the hospice Christmas Appeal. Again the above are examples of synergy in action. I feel proud and happy to have played a part in raising the £3 million target to build Keech Cottage, a truly special place for children.

Carol Bagni
Fundraising Manager (1998 - 2000)

Chapter Ten

Making it happen

"Despite the damp and miserable
weather on the day of the official
opening, there was plenty to cheer
about as HRH The Princess Royal
arrived at Keech Cottage"

There was no better way to celebrate and reward everyone involved in the record-breaking three years of fundraising than a Royal opening of the new children's hospice. The new millennium marked the extension of the existing (and very successful) community nursing service for children to include a purpose-built facility for those who needed care other than at home.

Keech Cottage Children's Hospice officially opened on 28th March 2000. Since then it has served the local community by providing care and support to children diagnosed with life-limiting illnesses. From the moment a child's condition is diagnosed, the now combined community and in-house hospice service provided care for families facing the loss of their child; helped families to care for their sick child through their illness and into the family's bereavement; and then continued to 'be there' for as long as necessary afterwards. Keech Cottage prided itself on its ability to support the entire family and help them make the most of their limited time together. Following the opening and over the years to come, many families were to describe the new building as an oasis of calm in their hectic, stressful and sometimes very sad lives. For parents especially, only the hospice could appreciate the insidious effects of caring for a child whose condition could deteriorate over many years, who would most likely die ahead of them, and whose dreams and possibilities for the future would be very limited.

The Royal opening

HRH The Princess Royal officially opened Keech Cottage Children's Hospice, the twenty-second children's hospice to open in Britain.

Despite the damp and miserable weather on the day of the official opening, there was plenty to cheer about as HRH The Princess Royal arrived at Keech Cottage. Pupils form Bramingham and William Austin primary schools waved butterflies, the national emblem of children's hospices, and cheered the Princess as she unveiled a plaque in the main entrance to commemorate her visit.

The honour of presenting flowers to the Princess went to 11-year-old Sam Coleman from Dunstable, who was suffering from muscular dystrophy and stayed at the hospice for the first time the weekend before the official opening. His mum, Louise, said to *Luton & Dunstable Herald & Post*:

A scene from the
Royal opening

"Children are free to be children..."

"He thinks it's great. The nurses asked him if he would like to stay again sometime and he said, 'Yeah, next weekend?' I wouldn't dream I was in a hospice – it's like a hotel. In hospitals you have to be quiet and watch what you are doing, but not here. Children are free to be children. There is so much for them to do and they get one-to-one care from the nurses who are all really lovely."

During her hour-long tour of the building, Princess Anne met 19 families cared for by Keech Cottage, staff and a selection of fundraisers who had helped raise money for the appeal. Before leaving she planted a tree outside the entrance in memory of Lisa Nolan, who died in 1995, aged 15. Lisa's mother, Anna, from Dunstable, had been actively campaigning for a children's hospice in Bedfordshire. A then local primary school pupil, Ami Witchard, is today one of the youngest employees at the hospice. She remembers well her first visit to Keech:

"Aged seven I came with my school, Bramingham Primary to the Royal opening of Keech Cottage. It was a damp and windy day, but this didn't affect how excited we were. Each of us waved a little England flag waiting to see her. She arrived two hours late and walked up, picked up a shovel and quickly put some mud on to a new tree that had been planted. That's how I remember it! My second visit to Keech was on 26th May 2011. Eleven years on and aged 18, I was being interviewed for the place of an apprentice here at Keech. I am now working for Keech Hospice Care and am thoroughly enjoying working with the people I do, and of course I love being an apprentice here! Eleven years after meeting HRH Princess Anne, I will be here for another big event for Keech, the 21 year anniversary in 2012."

Princess Anne talking with Iris White and hospice founder, Dr Wink White

Princess Anne planted a tree in front of Keech Cottage

Room to grow

Keech Cottage was the third hospice building project the charity had completed, just under 10 years since the original, Betty Robinson House, opened in 1991, and almost five years since the second, the Powdrill Centre, a day hospice and out-patient extension for adults, opened its doors in 1996.

Now, with both the adult and children's hospice operational on the same site, the charity could provide a unique service for patients of all ages. With the best facilities for children, at Keech Cottage, to this day sick children could enjoy the maximum amount of fun, friendship and quality of life in the short time they have. The specialist facilities included a day care area, computer room, wet play area, multi-sensory room, games room and five bedrooms. The hospice provided plenty of opportunities for play and recreational activities, ensuring the children would have as much fun as possible, while receiving the best medical care available. On completion, Keech Cottage was a service of which the community could be proud. General Manager Martin Johnson said:

"The opening of Keech Cottage is a tribute to the common sense and determination of the hospice trustees, the enthusiasm of the thousands who were involved in fundraising, as well as the architects and builders, and all the hospice professionals and specialist team who together have worked to produce such a centre for care."

112

'Very Special Place'

" A stay at the hospice provided us with the get-up-and-go to cope again."

Shortly after the opening, the Long family from Stevenage were the first family to spend a week at Keech Cottage. Lily Long, just six years old, suffered from a unique condition that doctors could not diagnose and had multiple disabilities. Her parents had to feed her through a tube overnight and could not go anywhere without an oxygen supply. "Lily needs a tremendous amount of care," explained her father Steve.

"It's a 24-hour a day job. I've had to give up work to help look after her. My wife Pam and I rarely get a chance to go out together. After a while it can get too much and that's when we need the children's hospice."

During their week at Keech Cottage, Steve and Pam had a chance to relax and unwind, safe in the knowledge that the care team were looking after Lily and her older brother Adam.

"It was great having no worries for a week. Not having to worry about getting Lily's medicines ready or struggling to bath her before bed...

"...Just getting a full night's sleep was a luxury."

"...Plus the kids love it here. The facilities are brilliant, there's always a happy atmosphere and the staff get on so well. The minute you walk in they put you at ease. It's just what we all need."

S teve and Pam, like many of the families who used Keech Cottage form the early days, wanted to ensure Lily could make the most of the short time she had left. While they would have liked to do everything themselves they realised that to maintain the pace of life needed, they must have regular breaks to 'recharge' their batteries.

> *"A stay at the hospice provided us with the get-up-and-go to cope again. They're a very special place."*

From the very start, Keech Cottage cared for the whole family and this included a service dedicated to the needs of siblings. Martin Johnson reflected on the importance of such innovations:

> *"It's easy to see how badly damaged some sibling relationships are by the experience of growing up with an incurably sick sibling. The parents have to give much of their attention to the sick child, often leaving the well child to deal with some complex feelings of neglect or envy. We felt that if we could do something to help siblings through these times we could potentially be doing a lot of good."*

Mike Keel, the Director of Nursing at the time, said:

> *"Any family in Hertfordshire or Bedfordshire who has been given the awful news that their child has a life-limiting condition, now has somewhere to turn. All members of the family (and family friends) experience a whole range of emotions, stresses and difficulties arising from having a dying child in their midst. They need to know that these feelings are normal and there is 'light at the end of the tunnel.'*

> *"It is rewarding as a nurse to know that our community wants to help these families give their children the best during their short life. Parents only have one chance to get it right and where possible they want to do it themselves, but sometimes they need a helping hand and that's what we offer – discreet help, particularly after their child has died and they feel utter despair."*

The first Keech Cottage informational leaflet

Interior of newly built Keech Cottage

John Maddox, left, saying 'goodbye' to Dr David Siegler

New Chairman

The long awaited opening brought changes to the charity's boardroom too. Six days before the opening on the 22nd March 2000, the Board of Trustees elected John Maddox as their new Chairman, succeeding Dr David Siegler.

John had been involved with the hospice since 1994, both as a trustee and chairman of the Midsummer Show Committee. Formally the Director of Leisure & Amenities at Luton Borough Council, he was also a well known figure throughout the local community. Speaking of his new position John said:

"I'm humbled by this appointment. Over the last six years I've seen the hospice go through a period of rapid expansion. Now I believe we must consolidate our position, redefine the appropriateness of what we have to offer and maintain the excellence for which we are already noted. I'd like to thank Dr Siegler for steering the hospice so successfully during his term in office. I'm looking forward to meeting many of our supporters over the next few months."

More than 20 years on, John, who was later appointed the Deputy Lord Lieutenant of Bedfordshire, remembered the excitement:

"Dr David Seigler, Chairman of the last six years, was exceptionally busy as the day for our Royal visitor approached and ecstatic in the news that it was to be Her Royal Highness, The Princess Royal. The day was magnificent, everything went like clockwork and the news coverage seemed to spur the entire community for one last fundraising push to complete furnishings for bedrooms, play areas and gardens. Being asked to introduce Her Royal Highness to several guests paraded on the landing was the highlight for me as it had been the Board's decision two days earlier to afford me the honour of the Chair as David was to step down and retire from service."

Dennis Keech O.B.E

A major benefactor to the children's hospice

Dennis Keech has lived in Luton for almost 60 years and has been dedicated to Bedfordshire and to developing manufacturing and creating jobs.

He was a founder member of Camford Engineering in 1964, a company that grew into a multi-million group employing over 2,000 people. Mr Keech resigned from Camford in 1990 and acquired Metalen Hospitality Furniture. He also acquired Automold Ltd in Stroud, Gloucestershire, a company supplying components to the European motor industry.

Mr Keech along with others saved the A.C.Delco wiper business in Dunstable, Bedfordshire from closure and became a Director of A.C.D Tridon's parent company. In 1996 the Queen honoured Dennis with an O.B.E. for 'Services to the Motor Manufacturing Industry'.

At the time of Keech Cottage opening, his businesses were all administered by Latimer Associates and covered many and varied areas from manufacturing to property, from telecommunications to design. Mr Keech is married and lives with his wife Shirley in Luton. They have two sons, who are both involved in the businesses, and four grandchildren.

Shirley Keech has for many years been involved in the local amateur music scene and is responsible for recognising the need and sowing the seed for the creation of a local hospice for children.

Dennis Keech

Our little *barnacle*

Abbie & Declan's Story

Abbie Brandon (top) and the Brandon Family

" Keech is, and always will be a *Special* part of our lives. "

When Abbie came into our world, we thought our family, which also included our two-year old son, Reece, was complete. It was a huge shock for us when, at just 8 days old, Abbie was admitted to hospital with dehydration. After further investigation, we were told Abbie would be blind and brain damaged. As devastating as that was to hear, worse was to follow. After several more hospital admissions, at 8 months old, Abbie was diagnosed with Cocaine Syndrome. We were told this meant she would suffer from delayed development, visual and hearing impediments, sun sensitivity, short stature and a life expectancy age of around 5-7 years old. Although Abbie could never do things like laugh, babble, talk or support herself, her face would light up when you stroked her cheek or tickled her.

She loved to be massaged or to feel the vibrations of music through her feet but most of all she loved being cuddled – she was our little barnacle. When we were first told about Keech, when Abbie was just over a year old, we wondered what they would be able to do for us. Little did we know that this was the place which would carry us through some very uncertain times. After our first visit, Abbie received care at the hospice and at home. Reece was always welcomed and all of us enjoyed using the hydrotherapy pool. Whenever Abbie was at Keech we were entirely at ease and when a nurse came to our house this gave us the chance to spend some quality time with Reece.

During her short life, Abbie had many illnesses and then, having contracted septicaemia and pneumonia, we had to face her last days. She died, aged just 21/2 and we took her to the Meadow Suite at Keech. We put her to bed and gave her a kiss goodnight before going home. We returned the next morning, after grandparents had arrived to sit with Reece, and took some of Abbie's personal things and toys for her bed. The staff at Keech were there to comfort us and helped us with the legal side of things too. They were fantastic and we couldn't have got through such a time without them.

Since then, we've spoken to grief counsellors and attended group support sessions at Keech. When you have a child with a very complex disability, hospitals become such a part of your life and when that child dies the contact stops. But with Keech, the care and support is still there, for as long as you need it. Words cannot express the value Keech has for our family. We are so grateful for Abbie and, although her life was short, we have met so many wonderful people because of her. Keech is, and always will be, a special part of our lives.

Misti and Matt, Abbie's Mum and Dad

At just 31/2 months old, our son, Declan, was diagnosed with Lissencephaly. That's a rare brain formation disorder which literally means 'smooth brain'. For Declan that meant he had constant seizures and lots of chest problems throughout his life. We were introduced to Keech when Declan was about 6 months old and I remember thinking 'no, he wasn't going to a hospice, that's where people go to die'. But, I soon saw that wasn't the case. Keech was actually somewhere which allowed him to live.

After that, Declan had lots of health complications and we were in and out of Keech all the time. In 2006, when he was 4 years old, Declan became very poorly and then about a year later his medication was switched to palliative care only. His condition got steadily worse and on 13th December 2008 he was transferred from the hospital to Keech for his last few days. In the early hours of 15th December he grew tired of fighting and fell asleep forever. He was just 61/2 years old. Keech did so much to help us through this terrible time. They called our Priest in and knew what was needed to make us comfortable. They looked after us in every way. The expert care and love which Keech gave to our family (and gives to all the families they look after) made the transition of Declan no longer being with us much easier. At the end we knew Declan was finally safe and it was Keech which made a very sad experience into something that we can look back on as beautiful and peaceful. For that, we will be indebted to Keech forever.

Caroline Kelly, Declan's Mum

Declan with a Keech nurse

Chapter Eleven

Steaming ahead

> "The Board of Trustees had quietly approved work to extend the In-patient Unit of Betty Robinson House."

From left to right: Fundraising Manager Roger Sharp, Betty Robinson, Marjorie Steel and Matron Barbara Kettley at the Betty Robinson house

After the Royal opening, one could mistakenly assume, the hospice had time to reflect on the overwhelming success of Keech Cottage or relish the fact that its total time from concept to completion was less than two years. It wasn't the way of the charity, however.

During 1999, in all the hustle and bustle of what had been a building site for many months, the Board of Trustees had quietly approved work to extend the In-patient Unit of Betty Robinson House. This extension involved converting one of the adult unit's four bedded bays into four separate rooms to comply with proposed new government regulations and provide patients with a greater degree of privacy. Despite it being only ten years from initial design, bathrooms, hoist regulation and water supply pipes were all falling short of modern day standards and requirements. The new rooms were, therefore, to upgrade the facilities generally and to connect both the Powdrill Day Hospice and Keech Cottage through a new 'sunny' sitting room to allow patients to interact with others and also to provide access into the hospice's beautiful gardens.

New improvements for the hospice

Marjorie Steel, daughter of the Powdrills, and Betty Robinson's cousin, had been a patient in these ageing facilities before being moved to a nearby nursing home where she sadly died. The cost of the proposed extension was £150,000 and on hearing these figures the Trustees of The Steel Charitable Trust granted the full amount as a memorial to Marjorie and were all present at the opening of the Marjorie Steel wing on 24th May 2000. It was a fitting tribute to Marjorie who in 1996 had been present at the opening of The Powdrill Day Hospice in memory of her own parents and a reminder that together with her own trustees had, by the time of completing this facility, contributed over £1 million to the capital build and running costs of the hospices. After the official opening, Shirley Gadsden, Nurse Team Leader at the time, said:

"This new extension means we can offer private rooms on a more regular basis and the sitting room will help us forge much closer links with Day Care and Keech Cottage for a fully integrated service".

One of the rooms, The Lavender Room, was furnished by members of Luton Inner Wheel Club of which Marjorie had been an active participant. The Steel Charitable Trust's financial funds accumulated from the sale of farmland on the Eastern side of Luton formerly owned by the Powdrill family. Robert and Marjorie Steel, a childless couple, established the Trust in 1976 and as the land was disposed of for housing development the fund grew to support other major Luton projects at the Luton and Dunstable Hospital, The University of Bedfordshire, St Mary's Parish Church, Bushmead Church and The Salvation Army. Robert Steel died in 1983 and Marjorie continued to administer the funds supported by four trustees.

Facing the challenges

'We went for *Gold*, when we should have gone for *Bronze*.'

The euphoria of the Royal visit and the opening of this new wing quickly dissipated because the hydrotherapy pool was still unfinished. Only the shell had been built and then 'mothballed' to save costs until an appropriate source of funds could be found. Now with two hospices to fund, the trustees knew that any money to finish the pool had to be 'new' money and not detract from the general fund for the running costs of the two hospices. There was a feeling the public of Luton and South Bedfordshire were fatigued following the mammoth capital appeal for Keech Cottage and might not be able to sustain the increased running costs. The Chairman of Trustees at the time, John Maddox, remembered:

"Vandalism attacks to windows of the children's hospice construction site meant that my first report to the Board was full of continuous bad news. If this was not sufficient the General Manager, Martin Johnson, also announced he was moving on to another charity in his home town of St Neots as early as July. Such was the cash flow problem in late summer that I had to ask to delay some of the payments on the new building for two months so we could pay the staff.

Unfinished hydrotherapy pool in 2000

Of course we had already stopped any unnecessary expenditure, frozen vacant posts and appealed to the wider public of Bedfordshire and Hertfordshire for help. Thoughts of redundancies so soon after being fully staffed were relieved when I received a call from a solicitors firm telling me the charity had been left a £600,000 legacy. The legacy was from the estate of the now deceased, Betty Robinson. How fitting that once again, even in death, Betty Robinson secured the future of the charity with a gift."

The fundraising team, still led by Carol Bagni, was strengthened to take on the challenge of the new income targets. The Chair and Trustees relied heavily on Mike Keel, the Nursing Director of the day, and Joan Gray, the Business and Administration Director, to hold everything together while they searched for a replacement General Manager. Tim Watson, now in his tenth year as a trustee, became the Vice Chairman.

Joan Gray remembered that the children's unit had opened with a blaze of publicity with 21 staff in place ready to go. The capital appeal for the building had been so successful and high profile that everyone was swept up in it and once the building was finished a lot of supporters said to themselves: "Phew, that was tough but we've done it and now deserve a rest". Many supporters moved onto other charities and projects. In fact the appeal should have continued a little longer to put enough money in the bank to pay the running costs for a few months. But, as financial pressure hit the charity, it was becoming clear how this might have been a step too far. Joan Gray recalls:

"With hindsight, it would have been better to have done things on a smaller scale and got the unit fully running on a piece-by-piece basis. We went for gold, when we should have gone for bronze."

Although the opening of the children's hospice was in many ways a huge achievement, at one point the financial burden of building costs and continuing running costs came close to bringing the charity to its knees. Joan added:

"It was especially difficult because there was no-one leading the charity at that time. Martin Johnson had left but a replacement had yet to be found. I knew some of the finances but was not aware of the full severity of the situation. Then one day I heard a girl who worked in finance coming off the phone with a big sigh. I asked her what was wrong and found out that she had a draw full of bills to pay but there was no money in the bank!"

Joan called a meeting with Chairman, John Maddox and Eric Fountain who decided the charity's only option was to ask the bank for an overdraft. Knowing that there was still some residue to come from Betty Robinson's estate, the bank manager was sympathetic and the overdraft was agreed.

"How fitting that once again, even in death, Betty Robinson secured the future of the charity with a gift."

Wages were paid and although it had been a particularly rough road, for now the day was saved. With good news from the financial side, everyone seemed to be pulling their weight to keep going no matter what. The hundreds of visitors to open days and the interest of BBC Look East and Anglia Television and the many articles the hospice team managed to get into local papers.

For John, this showed a degree of success and growing interest in the charity's overall service. After much deliberation the Board of Trustees decided to seek the assistance of a London based recruitment firm who were adept at seeking senior management for the hospice world and they agreed to help with the process. It was to take until almost Christmas 2000 to interview and appoint John Quill as the new Chief Executive. John Maddox remembered:

" *The board* were adamant that, for the situation we now faced, John was our man with the right financial qualifications, a broad experience of life and, as a former Parish priest, compassionate to deal with patients, families and staff alike. John had also spent time in industry, local government and, during his priesthood days, he was also the Social Responsibility Officer for the Worcester Diocese for ten years. With Christmas and New Year approaching, I for one, hoped for more than an apple and orange in my Christmas stocking. Indeed, some good news for 2001, would be very welcome."

A turned corner

John Quill recalls his start as the new Chief Executive:

"I was actively looking to develop my career through a new CEO position and it was great when I was offered the job here. However, when I arrived at the charity I realised the accounts weren't quite adding up and in the summer of 2001, I went public with a deficit of £1 million! Well you can imagine the effect that had. I was interviewed live in the morning by Jon Gaunt on Three Counties Radio and then had to face a media scrum over the charity's position including some live television. I had said I wanted a challenge and that was what I got!

"As it happens we were saved by a timely bequest from the estate of Betty Robinson, who had given the land in the first place. That allowed me to pick myself and the charity up and get on with the job of increasing income through better relationships with local healthcare commissioners and by building up the fundraising team to raise more income, not least for the children's hospice that had not long been open and had cost more to build than had been raised. People were hugely supportive and we went from strength-to-strength from then on."

The hospice's new front man, together with the Chairman, John Maddox, appealed to the wider public via the local press with the full story. This only stimulated all and sundry to attack some of the now historic problems of the past. John Maddox recalled:

"When Jon Gaunt interviewed us both on Three Counties Radio, he asked me, in his loudest voice, if I was going to resign. I boldly replied that I had only just started, there was much to sort out and I was here to stay for a while at least. This exposure over the Three Counties area seemed to do the trick and during the next twelve months, from a deficit situation, when some beds in both the adult and children's hospices had to be closed, we produced a budget barely in the black but encouraging all the same. Staff morale also increased as we discovered that John Quill was more than a financial expert, compassionate leader and 'good egg' but was also capable of holding a note in song and, together with game staff member Jeff Lewcock, was prepared to entertain staff and volunteers in a light-hearted celebration of the year. I was just happy to direct the entertainment and draw a deep breath that perhaps we had turned the corner. Such hopes were only slowly beginning to look real. Although the publicity meant the hospice had managed to accumulate some funds, the target of around £660,000 to finish the hydrotherapy pool was still out of reach. The Trust Fundraiser at the time, Dominic Munro-McCarthy was tasked with trying to find the funds necessary.

"Dominic struck up a very friendly dialogue with one Trust who went on to become the lead donor with a contribution of £450,000. Sixteen others made up the rest of the amount needed. These trusts were adamant that the charity should not reduce the specification of the pool in anyway and that it should be the best it could be. This money was only available for building works and therefore would not have been given to the charity for running costs.

"So many people and organisations had shown an interest in using the pool once it was finished and this gave us the confidence that most of the estimated £20,000 per annum running costs would be covered by the fees they would pay.

"Work proceeded quickly throughout 2001 with all involved overawed by the quality of facilities as they emerged from the greyness that had been the concrete shell of the main tank. The finished article, as we all know today, is a splendid facility applauded by everyone who uses it and admired by not only the hospice world but all those smaller groups and charities that benefit from weekly use."

Before the £660,000 were secured, what had already been created was a tank measuring 16.5 x 7.0 m to be designed to cater for the needs of the disabled and frail of all ages. If the hospice could bring it to fruition, it would be of great value to the nursing staff in their day-to-day work. With advice from hydrotherapists, designers, the England Paralympic swimming coach and patients and their families, it was hoped that the scheme would be a shining example for other hospices to follow.

Cash problems: £2m surplus is now a £1m deficit

Beds may go in hospice crisis

AUDITORS have uncovered a huge deficit in the finances of Luton's Pasque Hospice.

Spending has transformed what was claimed to be a £2 million surplus just four years ago into a £1 million deficit.

There is only enough money to pay staff wages for the next two months and there are fears that the 10-bed facility for terminally ill adults will be cut to six.

Commenting on reports that bed closures were on the cards, chief executive John Quill said: "I want my tenure to be as open as possible and that's why I must comment on the bed-cutting reports.

"Because of our cash situation and general recruitment problems we can't have as many nurses as we would like. That means not all the beds will be available all the time.

"You can blame cash and recruitment problems for that."

The recent addition of the five-bed £4 million Keech Cottage children's hospice, which incorporates a teaching/conference centre, is being blamed for the problems. Barbara Kettley, a former matron at the Pasque, in Bramingham Road, Streatley, said: "Keech Cottage was more about ego than reality, but the trustees wouldn't listen and now there is a full-blown crisis.

"Transforming a £2 million surplus into a £1 million debt is truly devastating news, but the people of Luton have to rally round and overcome this crisis. I am just glad that the new chief executive, John Quill, immediately ordered this audit and uncovered what has been happening."

Part of the financial problem is a warning from the auditor that operation of the conference/teaching centre could attract the attentions of the VAT man.

One of Mr Quill's first actions since taking over as chief executive from Martin Johnson was to order an outside company to conduct an audit. Previous audits had been carried out by local companies who gave their services free, but the growth of the project made this no longer possible.

The hospice relies in large part on public fund-raising, charity events, donations from sympathetic firms and around 15 to 20 per cent financial support from the NHS.

Rumblings that all was not well at the hospice have surfaced intermittently jdkldklsa

Turn to Back Page

The Pasque Hospice with chief executive John Quill, below

In the local news: hospice crisis

A hydrotherapy pool...

A hydrotherapy pool is very different to a public swimming pool with water temperatures maintained at a higher rate, 34°C to stimulate circulation and relaxation but also to allow frail patients with poor temperature control the opportunity to experience water activities. Air temperature also has to be closely controlled at 28°C to avoid the 'shiver effect' and coldness when emerging whilst hoists, ramps and specially designed changing rooms allow privacy, dignity and as much independence as possible and were all essential to the scheme. With sensory lighting, sound systems to allow patients to exercise to music or listen to relaxing sounds whilst receiving hydrotherapy, the hospice was definitely creating a 'beacon' for the hospice world. John Maddox remembered:

> "Already supporting over 100 life-limited children and their families in Keech Cottage and approximately 40 adult Day Hospice clients who could regularly benefit from pool use we knew that the many other groups who had expressed interest in pool sessions may well be accommodated. Confirmed interest from Luton and Dunstable Hospital and from a number of residential homes also encouraged us to press on estimating that we might offer fifteen sessions per week for community groups and individuals, perhaps, as many as 7,000 per year. "

The grand opening took on a less than Royal affair but it was nonetheless an important moment, when parents Nicola and Mike Remond and patient Ron Young and his daughter cut the ribbon to declare the facility officially open in February 2002, just two years after the main building had passed its Royal test.

Meanwhile, the rest of the new complex which included the now named Fountain Suite for conferences and seminars, together with the Pool Suite and other small meeting rooms were being actively promoted as a source of income. With facilities for 120 delegates, audio visual presentations, exhibition space, administrative support services, secure parking and disabled access they offered some of the best resources in the North of the Borough of Luton and of appeal to the Luton and Dunstable Hospital and businesses in South Bedfordshire. The staff member responsible for the facility, Jeff Lewcock, was busy promoting the fact that Keech was one of a few hospices to have such facilities, especially of this quality, providing a range of luncheons and refreshments to complement any 'Away Day' requirement. However, John Maddox remembered that, despite its attractiveness, the facility was slow to return the investment:

> "I reflected at the time that Martin Johnson had said as he departed, don't worry you will get £100,000 from these facilities but, he didn't tell me or Jeff it would take nearly five years before that goal was achieved."

Although the conference facility was closed in later years, the new facilities have proved to be a valuable additional source of income and especially useful for their original purpose of training staff. Due to its size and general ambience, the facilities have been utilised for flower festivals, Christmas 'Lights of Love' events, presentations and visiting regional and national organisations not only requiring the flexibility that the range of rooms offered but also to experience the quality of an integrated service only offered at four other establishments in the country.

Along with generating funds, the conference facility had one special advantage – it was an opportunity to welcome on site visitors and businesses, who would not normally have a direct reason to visit the hospice. John Maddox commented:

Cutting the ribbon at the hydrotherapy pool opening

"I personally spent many a long and anxious Board meeting in these facilities but also many enjoyable occasions too, not the least of which, were the annual volunteers' evenings, the initial AGM meetings and all of the events that required the culinary skills of long serving catering manager, Liz Bradley."

The ups and downs of the hospice story have always come thick and fast. The opening of the hydrotherapy pool in February 2002 was quickly followed by the warehouse fire that destroyed over £80,000 of stock destined for the charity's nine shops. However, such was the response of the public and a generous offer of new premises in Luton's Britannia Estate the warehouse was soon up and running again. Within days the charity had also heard that a government New Opportunities Fund would commence in March, at least providing some hope that the projected budget for 2002/03 should break even and some of the closed beds might reopen.

Finished hydrotherapy pool

Charlotte's Story

"Our last hours together were in comfort and peace..."

Back in the summer of 2001 at the age of 6 years old. My Mum and Dad were visiting and picked Charlotte and her sister Becky up from school. My Dad commented that he thought Charlotte needed a new pair of shoes. He said it looked like one of her feet had grown and it was making her leg turn in. I thought: "It's the end of term, I'll throw the shoes away and sort a new pair out in the holidays". However the comment prompted Tony, my husband, and I to watch our daughter more carefully. Whilst away on holiday we noticed that Charlotte's leg turn seemed to be getting worse.

I made an appointment with our doctor. I thought maybe we were overeacting but the doctor referred us to the hospital nevertheless. During the short period of time between the doctor's appointment and the hospital appointment the leg turn and Charlotte's overall dexterity seemed to be getting worse. We saw the consultant at the hospital who completed a few tests but he didn't seem to be over worried.

Three months passed and we went back for a follow-up at the hospital. By this stage we had attended a parent's evening at Bushmead School and reading through Charlotte's work and comparing it to earlier pieces of work, it flagged that something was just not right. The hospital tests had not highlighted anything wrong but Dr Thomson suggested that Charlotte should have a CT scan. I remember it well, we had just returned back from Wales and on December 1st 2002 Charlotte had her first scan. By this time she was very wobbly and needed an escorting arm to get her about without her falling or bumping into things. Surprisingly, but to our relief, Charlotte's scan came back clear. However, this still left the unanswered question of what was happening to our lovely daughter.

At her next hospital appointment, Charlotte saw a Neurological consultant from Addenbrookes hospital. He too looked at the scans and said they were clear and suggested Charlotte should have physiotherapy which would help to build up her core strength. Mr Parker (Dr Nosey as Charlotte called him) told us he would now be doing a series of blood tests that would be used to eliminate a list of potential neurological conditions.

Physiotherapy took place on a weekly basis and Trisha, Charlotte's physiotherapist, visited Charlotte's school with me to suggest a care plan be put in place for Charlotte to assist her whilst there. The school, as ever, was very supportive and the Head set up a meeting with the local Education Department to apply for help for Charlotte whilst she was at school and to put in wheelchair access so Charlotte could continue to be schooled there. Charlotte's condition set about changes in the school which now allows them to deal with disabled children rather than having to exclude them. As we moved through 2003, further blood tests and discussions with Mr Parker continued and in the summer it was suggested Charlotte should be tested for Niemen Pick, a neurological disease which works on destroying muscle tissues and claiming life at an early age.

We had a routine visit to Addenbrookes to see Mr Parker on December 1st and as that date approached we could only think the worst as Charlotte's condition rapidly deteriorated. She was now getting around in a wheelchair, however overall she was happy, carefree and positive. We went in to see Mr Parker and we could see he was shocked at how Charlotte looked. He immediately sent her for an MRI scan and that night we found out what was wrong. Charlotte had a brain tumour, medulloblastoma was the technical term, and this was located in the cerebellum, the part of the brain which controls movement. This was obviously a big shock but at last we had something which, although it had its risks, could be treated. Within a couple of days Charlotte was operated on and, after a five and half hour operation, the

127

tumour was successfully removed. This unfortunately was not the end of the story. The tumour was malignant and Charlotte now had 18 months of radio and chemotherapy to endure. Endure she did and by 2006, life for Charlotte and the rest of us was starting to look more positive. We took a holiday to Italy in the summer. Charlotte walked again for the first time in 18 months and her hair was coming back shiny and lush. We were having routine scans every 3 months and all was looking good until the scan on Friday 8th September 2006.

I was sitting at my desk on the Monday afternoon when I received a call from Charlotte's Consultant. He didn't mess about and told me there and then that Charlotte had another tumour. I think I screamed and the office went deadly silent. The phone call to Tony and the journey home were unbearable. Only that morning Charlotte had excitely gone off on a week's school trip. Tony and I went to Addenbrookes Hospital early Tuesday morning to meet up with the Oncology team. The story was not good. There was very little experience of re-occurring brain tumours and treatment was not really tested. We had to choose whether we wanted to go ahead with treatment with a less then 5% chance of success. Charlotte returned from her school trip on a high. Singing school trip songs, we went off to the gym for the regular Friday night swimming lessons. She was none the wiser and having a ball. Saturday night we gathered Charlotte and Becky together to have the family chat. Charlotte in her brave and positive manner shrugged her shoulders and looked at us as if to say: "OK we've done this before, we can do it again."

The treatment Charlotte went through was incredibly tough, another five hour operation to remove the tumour and then chemotherapy treatment so harsh she was kept isolated in a room at Addenbrookes for four months to prevent infection. I stayed at the hospital whilst Tony, Becky and Tony's Mum did the 40 mile round trip after school and work every day. My tough brave little girl yet again got through this awful treatment and in March 2007 we came home not really knowing what we were to face.

Early in May, when we were out on a family trip, the car went over a speed bump and Charlotte mentioned her head felt strange. Tony glanced knowingly at me but didn't say anything. The doctors had already said there was no further treatment Charlotte would be able to have. She had already had two heavy courses of chemotherapy and a very heavy dose of radiotherapy. A few weeks went by and Charlotte amazingly sat her year 6 SAT exams. We were approaching half term and a visit to Wales, chosen by Becky for her birthday.

I returned home from work and Charlotte was not feeling at all good. We called the doctor and he referred her straightaway to the Luton and Dunstable Hospital and notified the Oncologists at Addenbrookes. Charlotte was scanned at the L&D the following day but I think we already knew the answer. The tumour had returned and this time there was nothing we could do.

We came out of hospital and Charlotte wanted to go up to the school to say goodbye to her friends on the final day before half term started. She wasn't really well enough so Tony took her there for a quick visit. Little did the children or teachers know that this would be Charlotte's final farewell but something in me thinks my daughter already knew.

Charlotte died on Monday 28th May 2007. She even seemed to plan that just right as it was a bank holiday which meant all her family and friends could be with her at the end. That's where Charlotte story ends so you may be asking why is she featured in this hospice book?

Charlotte's palliative and community nurse very kindly suggested that Charlotte could be laid to rest at the hospice. Still in shock, Tony and I agreed, not really knowing what to expect. This was a massive help to us. We could visit Charlotte when we wished, with no cold impersonal funeral parlour to visit but a lovely room filled with music and Charlotte's favourite toys and possessions. This definitely helped Tony, myself and all of Charlotte's family and friends to start their grieving process for Charlotte in a positive way. Nothing will ever heal the hole that Charlotte has left but we thank the hospice for the use of that lovely room which allowed us to spend our last hours with Charlotte in comfort and peace before her burial.

Judith, Charlotte's Mum

" Nothing will ever heal the hole that Charlotte has left...

...But we thank the hospice for the use of that *Lovely room*

which allowed us to spend our last hours with

Charlotte in comfort and peace before her burial."

I discovered that my Dad had terminal lung cancer in November of 2007 and it was the most devastating news that I have ever had. Dad was not a hearts and flowers man and didn't want any sympathy. He had raced banger cars and been a lorry driver all his life and was very much no nonsense and no fuss but with a wicked sense of humour.

The cancer progressed quickly and he was admitted first to the Luton and Dunstable Hospital and then moved to the Keech hospice. I found that every time I visited him at the hospice, the staff were friendly and caring. At the time there was some construction work going on around the hospice, but even that was not intrusive. On several occasions, the staff always made you feel welcome and there was a cup of tea, a warm smile and sometimes even cake!!

On the day my Dad passed away, the staff were very supportive and gave my family, our friends and myself as much time as we needed to say goodbye as well as the offer of support continuing in the future.

On the anniversary of his death I received a card personally hand written to say that the staff were thinking of me at that difficult time, which was a total surprise and greatly appreciated. I just want to thank the staff at Keech for the supportive, caring and dignified manner of their work; it was a great comfort to me at a very difficult time in my life.

Margaret Pike

Chapter Twelve

Friendships of a lifetime

"People of all walks of life, from community groups and local companies to school children and media have all contributed to the growth and successes of the charity over the decades."

There is no doubt that, at the very core of the hospice's work, lies an abundance of community ties and relations, many of which have formed and blossomed into priceless friendships. During 21 years of the hospice's history, these relationships have played a vital part in fundraising, helping the hospice through the good and the turbulent times.

To Keech Hospice Care, there never seems an appropriate way to thank all of its supporters for their relentless effort. Looking back, it seems that hardly anyone in the local community has not supported the hospice in one way or another. People of all walks of life, from community groups and local companies to school children and media have all contributed to the growth and successes of the charity over the decades.

There are of course some who deserve a special mention and, to introduce these, the current Fundraising Director at the hospice, Jacqui Shepherd, said:

"There are so many people who warrant a mention and I have to apologise right now if inadvertently we've missed anyone out. But, there are some extra special friends that have shown a major level of dedication to Keech.

"Be it for their endless support, their courage or the faith they've shown in the hospice when the going got tough, these are the people who have been truly remarkable in the hospice's life."

Golf lovers *Love* their hospice

One of the earliest of these special relationships, going back to the build of the original adult hospice, is that which has formed between the charity and South Bedfordshire Golf Club.

With a number of the charity's earliest supporters also being members of the club (including Bruce Skinner, Jack Sapsworth, John Maddox and Peter Collins), the golfers began hosting a Golf Day for the hospice. The first event was held in May 1989 and, co-ordinated by Bruce Skinner, it raised around £3,000. After running the event for ten years, Bruce passed the baton on to Jack Sapsworth and the annual Golf Day has been held every year since. With such longevity in their support for the hospice, South Bedfordshire Golf Club has, to date, raised in the region of £250,000.

Over the years, many of the club's members have been through the doors of the hospice not only to present the cheques but sadly for personal reasons. One such notable member was Don Wall who became a patient and died at the hospice in November 2010. Don had been involved with the hospice from the early days and had engaged fellow builders from the Irish community to volunteer to clear the site on three separate occasions – for the building of the original adult hospice, the children's hospice and for the new adult In-patient Unit.

Several other golf clubs across the region have offered their support to Keech, one of the more recent being Chalgrave Manor. Although the club first made a donation to Keech back in 1998, things started in earnest in 2004 when the children's hospice was nominated as the fixed recipient of its fundraising activity. Since then, the club has held a Charity Golf Day every year and made a contribution of over £55,000 to date.

Steve Randall, the club's owner and Managing Director of Chalgrave Manor Golf Club Limited, is proud of the strong friendship:

"One of the things that has marked Keech Hospice Care as being exceptional has been the fact, that over the years, at our Captains Day in June, the outgoing Captain has presented his cheque to a representative of Keech, or a parent of a child who has been at or is at the hospice. On each and every occasion, the speech on what Keech stands for, what it does and why the support is so necessary is delivered with such passion and eloquence that none present can possibly feel that the work and the effort made for the previous year can be anything less for the coming year."

Standing together

As well as the good work undertaken by local golfers, a number of community focused groups and societies have shown a common interest in the work of the hospice. A lot have stood by the charity since the word go.

For more than 100 years Freemasons have supported hospice services in the UK...

...and, at the time of publication of this book, somewhere in the region of £600,000 has been raised for Keech Hospice Care through the Masonic movement across Hertfordshire, Bedfordshire, Buckinghamshire, Northamptonshire, North London and the National Masonic Grand Charity.

Funds have been raised through a variety of activities including ladies days and charity of the year adoptions and over the years Keech has been the grateful recipient of a constant stream of cheques from individual lodges.

Following the presentation of just one of the many grants awarded to Keech by the Freemasons' Grand Charity in February 2010, the Provincial Grand Master, Michael Sawyer said:

"Keech provides a vital service to the local community and we are pleased to support them in maintaining the highest level of care."

Michael admitted how proud the Freemasons of Bedfordshire are to have been associated with the hospice since its birth 21 years ago:

"Some of our lodges made donations in cash or by way of items for the comfort of the patients when the hospice first opened its doors. Since that time we have been pleased to have been able to make regular donations totalling around £600,000 as part of our Freemasonry in the Community initiative. We were also proud to have been able to help when Keech Cottage was built. It is our wish that Keech Hospice Care now goes from strength to strength as a vital part of the community and we will do our best to make this happen with our continued support. Long may the hospice prosper to comfort those in need."

Chief Executive, Mike Keel commented on how much Keech has been indebted to the Freemasons over the years:

"The Freemasons have shown such dedicated support to Keech Hospice Care and to have raised more than half a million is an amazing feat. The benefit this brings to the people who need our care at Keech is truly invaluable and for that, we are eternally grateful."

Back when the concept of a hospice for Luton and South Bedfordshire was first developed, it was no surprise that the Rotary clubs of the area were also quick to respond with fundraising activity.

Freemasons supporting the charity as reported in local newspapers from 1999 and 2010

A s early as 1988, four Luton clubs, Barton-Le-Clay, Flitwick, Ampthill and the two Dunstable clubs nominated the hospice amongst their chosen good causes and the partnership was off to a flying start. The Ladies Inner Wheel clubs did likewise.

The Rotary Club of Luton provided very early assistance through support from Geoffrey Squires, Tim Watson, Derek Hewitt, Bruce Skinner and Jack Sapsworth, all of whom brought their varied skills, experience and contacts to the charity. The Rotary Club of North Luton also came on board swiftly and Geoffrey Farr utilised his local government and business connections to good effect, especially when he volunteered to lead the corporate appeal for major funds. When Paul Denton, of Luton North became District Rotary Governor, he had the ear of over fifty Rotary and Inner Wheel Clubs from Flitwick to Potters Bar, something he used to actively promote the concept of palliative care and what the hospice was achieving. By matching District Rotary grants to local money, Paul also raised sufficient funds to buy the first ambulance for the hospice. The Rotary Clubs of Luton Chiltern, St Albans, Stevenage, Hitchin and Bedford, to name a few, became very supportive too.

Also hugely involved with the hospice were Rotarians: Peter Collins of the Luton Club, a member of the charity's Trading Company and regular driver for day hospice patients; Alan Bartram and Brian Williams who took on fundraising roles and supported major events; and Julia Siegler of the Someries Club who lent her practical support in the laundry room at the hospice, a role she still performs twenty years later!

All of these people and more were instrumental in inspiring their respective Rotary clubs to engage in constant fundraising and volunteering activities for the hospice. Even if fundraising fatigue was to set in, the Luton Clubs and Barton-Le-Clay would continue their involvement at the charity's annual Midsummer Show and with donations of money. Jack Sapsworth, who became Chairman of the Trading Company, had also formed a volunteer Fundraising Committee back in 1995.

Together with John Maddox and others, the committee went on to raise substantial amounts through Rotary boxing nights, sporting dinners, quiz nights, Chinese banquets, casino nights and the golfing events held in conjunction with South Bedfordshire Golf Club. Speaking of the lengths that Rotary has gone to for the hospice, John Maddox said:

> "Such has been the joint effort of many clubs in the District that I would suggest that the hospices have been one of the main focuses of all Rotary Presidents in their year of office and that it will continue to attract funds over future years. Clearly, the Rotary Club of Luton have made the hospices their centre of interest since those early days and each new President seems to have absorbed the urgency of being involved in this major community project. But then, the hospices and, indeed, the world hospice movement itself, have become a beacon of interest and necessity for so many. I am sure I speak for all those Rotarians and ladies of Inner Wheel when I reflect on the magnificent contributions of time and money made and the help it has brought to others in need. The motto of Rotary, 'Service Above Self' has been exemplary."

Singing for the hospice

Another group of people, this time all women, that has relentlessly supported the hospice is a choral group which sprang from those who had been members of the Luton Girls Choir and became 'Pasque Harmony'.

Back in the 1980s, Margaret Hale-Owens (or Margaret Patten as she was then) sang as a guest soloist at weddings and with orchestras and choirs, to raise funds for the Luton and South Beds Hospice. Following the loss of a good friend and benefactor of the hospice, Marjorie Steel, Margaret instigated a Millennium Memorial Project, in memory of both Marjorie and Arthur Davies MBE, founder and musical

Cheque presentation from the Rotary Club of Dunstable, Oct 1997

Director of The Luton Girls Choir, which Margaret had been a part of during her youth. The project involved creating an 18 track album entitled 'Music in my Heart' which raised a magnificent £21,000 for what was by then The Pasque Charity.

In November 2000, an album launch concert was held and supported by James Banville, the Vauxhall Male Voice Choir and Margaret's former Luton Girls Choir friends. The success of this project inspired Margaret's husband, Norman Owens, to realise his ambition of bringing the world renowned Morriston Orpheus Male Voice Choir to perform in Luton. In October 2002, Norman arranged a concert entitled 'On Wings of Song' in which Margaret and her friends performed to raise some of the funds necessary to bring the Welsh choir to Luton.

In April 2003, the Morriston Orpheus choir performed for the first time in Luton at a Gala Concert, raising £17,000 for the hospice. With Margaret supporting as guest soloist and other former members of the Luton Girls Choir helping with the front of house duties, it was at this event that they expressed their wish to be involved in future projects. A few months later, Margaret met with Wendy Beck, Lynda Davies, Alison Nicol and Wendy Welburn to discuss the creation of 'Pasque Harmony'. They approached the Chairman of the Pasque Charity and on referral to the trustees it was agreed they would form the choir. At the time this was the first in the country to be affiliated to a hospice.

Patron, Pam Rhodes receiving just one of the many cheques presented from a local Lodge

Pasque Harmony performed their first concert on 23rd November 2003 entitled 'A Little Night Music' at St Augustine's Church in Luton. Since then, Pasque Harmony has performed at concerts and weddings and recorded two CDs to raise funds for the charity. As well as contributing to the amount raised through subsequent concerts with the Morriston Orpheus Choir, alone Pasque Harmony have raised around £60,000 for the charity.

Choir member, Rita Gradon, first came into contact with Keech when she was working for a soft furnishing firm in Luton which supplied curtains for the children's hospice. Some years later, a friend who she knew from her time with the Ladies Vauxhall choir asked Rita if she could make some alterations to her new choir outfit and invited her to become part of Pasque Harmony. Having recently undergone a hip operation, Rita says she was unsure at first but decided to join and hasn't looked back since:

"I started to weigh up the pros and cons. My husband is a landlord and so worked most nights and my family had flown the nest and so I did have plenty of time. However I needed to get my confidence back. I had had MS for 36 years and since the operation I needed two crutches to walk. Walking out on stage like that was something else.

"I have been with the choir now for 6 years, during which time I have had four more operations and now have to sit down for the concerts, but the friendship of my colleagues and the support they have all given me, I cannot begin to express...

"I am honoured to be able to help to raise funds towards this fantastic hospice just by singing. Hopefully I will be able to continue to do what I love – singing and being part of an inspirational and passionate choir. Yes, it was the right decision to join Pasque Harmony!"

Preparing for the Concert Spectacular in 2005 Pasque Harmony members with Norman Owens, Robin Radford and John Maddox

In 2009 Pasque Harmony raised money to purchase one of the Jacuzzi baths in the new adult In-patient Unit

Charity begins at work

Whilst some have made it their business to support the hospices as part of their social or recreational life, others have chosen to take their backing for the charity into their place of work. Vauxhall is one of the local workplaces that has supported the hospice since it opened its doors. Over the years, the vehicle manufacturer has purchased valuable equipment, fundraised for day-to-day running costs, become involved at trustee level and since 1998 has regularly awarded the hospice with a vehicle to use. Every year the vehicle is exchanged for another brand new one and at this moment in time, the charity has the benefit of a Vauxhall Astra Sports Tourer.

Looking back to 1991 and a recession had hit most people in the UK. To promote their vehicles, Vauxhall ran a 'Talking Proud' programme which encouraged employees to spread the good word about Vauxhall Vehicles and also involved the company making a donation to the hospice for every vehicle sold through the programme. Because Vauxhall and its staff played a major role in making the four year dream of the hospice a reality, in January 1991 the doors of the hospice were opened to Vauxhall staff and pensioners, just to thank them for their commitment. Vauxhall had been the biggest commercial donor and Appeal Director, Geoffrey Farr, said:

"They were able to see how the money raised had been spent for the benefit of the terminally ill patients."

When it came to fundraising for the development of the children's hospice, the charity held an important event at the Vauxhall Recreation Club to inform local community, businesses and dignitaries of its plans. After many people had spoken of their experiences and most of the audience had got their handkerchiefs out, Eric Fountain, Director of Public Affairs at Vauxhall, stood up to say a few words and presented a cheque for £100,000. After much applause, the good feeling swept the room and, all of a sudden people were standing up and holding out cheques for various amounts of money. The whole room was buzzing!

Whilst Vauxhall employees have got involved in all kinds of fundraising activities for Keech, it's not just staff that has been encouraged to help. Reaching out to the wider community, in 2004, Vauxhall sponsored a reading challenge for children in Bedfordshire whereby, for every book read, they made a donation to the hospice. Some 14,300 youngsters took part, 110,880 books were read and that meant a donation of £4,500.

One of the early vehicles supplied by Vauxhall

Chief Executive Mike Keel receiving the Vauxhall car in 2011

For Vauxhall...

For Vauxhall, it was money well spent and the charity was in awe of the fantastic effort everyone had put in. In later years, sponsorship of the reading challenge was taken over by Whitbread but continued to benefit Keech. Nick Reilly, President of GM Europe and GM Executive Vice President, commented on the long standing relationship Vauxhall has maintained with the hospice:

The Bedfordshire reading challenge, as reported in the Vauxhall Mirror in 2004

The Talking Proud programme, as reported in The Vauxhall Mirror in 1991

"Vauxhall Motors has been connected in many ways to the hospice right from the beginning. There have been volunteer workers, several trustees and, of course patients, who have worked at Vauxhall at some time. Vauxhall is very pleased to have been involved directly or indirectly in helping such a commendable institution. Vauxhall is still an important employer in Luton, albeit on a smaller scale than in the past. We had to close an important manufacturing plant but it is pleasing to see the van manufacturing operations continuing strongly. We also keep the headquarters of Vauxhall in Luton together with many of the functions required to run such a business. It is important that a company such as Vauxhall plays a part in the wider community in which it resides and our association with the hospice is a good example of this.

"On behalf of Vauxhall Motors and all its employees, I would like to congratulate Keech Hospice Care and all involved in it over the years for its outstanding contribution to the local community and to its residents. I hope a successor of mine will be able to record similar congratulations after another 21 years."

Alongside Vauxhall, there are so many other local companies that have made the extra effort to help Keech continue its work over the years. While this list is in no way exhaustive, here's just some of the things those organisations and their staff have done.

Monarch Airlines helped Keech send its sponsored butterfly around the world by carrying it on one of their flights from Luton to Malaga back in 1999. Staff have participated in fundraising events for the charity and the airline has also donated many flight tickets which Keech has used as prizes in raffles, auctions and prize draws.

Arriva buses have provided its buses free of charge on many occasions, notably taking hundreds of ladies along to the women's walking challenge in Hyde Park some years back and helping to transport people to the hospice for its Light up a Life (previously Lights of Love) event every year. Arriva have also been major sponsors of the Keech lottery and offer further support by placing banners and posters on their buses to promote fundraising events.

In 2008, a business start-up in Stevenage, Snak Appeal, began offering work places and leisure establishments sweet and savoury snack boxes promoting the children's hospice. With each snack item selling for £1 and a significant percentage of sales going to Keech, the company was well on its way to raising £100,000 in 2011.

The Admiral Group has supported Keech for nearly ten years as a supplier of equipment, a donor and a sponsor for events. Over the years, the telecommunications company has been involved in sponsoring the hospice's team entry into the Flora Women's Challenge and the prestigious Butterfly Ball. More recently, Admiral provided a major part of the funding for a new mini-bus for Keech and, in total, the company has made a financial contribution of over £25,000 to the charity.

Having supported the charity from the early days, London Luton Airport chose Keech as its Charity of the Year for 2009 and 2010. During those years, staff held collections at the terminal, quiz nights, cake sales and recycling initiatives. Some ran marathons, others took part in the Midnight Walk or overseas treks and many of the airport's staff volunteered at the hospice itself, helping with cleaning tasks. By the end of 2010, the airport had become the hospice's largest corporate supporter, donating over £167,000 in its lifetime.

Roche UK, in Welwyn Garden City, who develop diagnostic and pharmaceutical medicines, chose Keech as its Charity of the Year for 2010, throughout which their staff got involved in everything from book sales to bungee jumps and banger rallies to talent contests! They also helped with volunteering projects and at the end of that year they donated a massive £41,428 towards the children's hospice.

Many local supermarkets have hosted Smiley Sam and other collections for Keech – notably Sainsbury's in Bramingham, Asda in Wigmore and Tesco in Dunstable, all of which have also adopted Keech as their Charity of the Year at some point. Sainsbury's in Bramingham also now donate their out-of-date flowers for the hospice flower arrangers to work their magic on.

Over the years, several companies have given some very large sums of money but many others have given their support in a wide variety of different ways – from companies like HSBC who have sponsored fundraising challenges to those like Whitbread and Wates who have volunteered to help with refurbishments. From the donations of thousands to the offer of a raffle prize, every means of support has played its part in helping Keech to keep its care services going.

As a charity champion for her place of work, firstly through First Choice and then Thomson Airways, Carly Swaine summed up her reasons for getting behind the hospice:

> "At First Choice, we all decided to support Keech as members of the crew had loved ones who were at the hospice and I had researched it a lot on the Internet and got quite close to it. Also, the fact that it involved children really touched our hearts. From then we collected unwanted foreign and British coins and notes from our aircraft based at Luton. Also, on the side, I decided to hold a Keech donation day in 2006 at my parents' house where we held a quiz and raised money. It was a fantastic day with perfect weather and everyone had a ball. We raised about £220 for to Keech.

> "In November 2007 our base closed so I had to go to Stansted but then we merged Airlines with Thomson and became Thomson Airways. I was then able to come back to Luton and I again volunteered for the role of charity champion. When I was with First Choice I really became close and fond of the hospice and its staff so I really wanted to continue supporting Keech. I hope to continue this in the future."

Luton Town Football Club has held collections and given their Charity Shield money to the hospice for many years.

One of the newest corporate supporters, Charles Wells and Young of Bedford, have raised significant sums of money already and a new Keech Birthday brew is also being produced!

The local media group, Premier Newspapers, have been extremely supportive in giving coverage to news and features about the hospice.

Mayoral adoptions have regularly come in from across the local region and many local public houses have got their punters in on the fundraising act. Some, like the Hen and Chickens in Baldock have given year-round support, holding fun days, Golf Days, raffles and more to raise £55,000.

Little big friends

In addition to the support of the corporate world, Keech has greatly benefitted from the interest shown by schools, colleges, scouts, guides, youth groups and other young people's organisations.

As well as providing a venue for fundraising events and making its car park available for Light up a Life year after year, Barnfield College has encouraged its staff and pupils to get involved with the hospice. They've held fundraising dinners, volunteered at events, taken part in Christmas campaigns such as sharing a giant card and making donations to the hospice, set charity challenges for its students and volunteered in the adult day care unit, providing therapies and beauty treatments.

Taking both the free venue provision and the support provided by staff and students into consideration, Barnfield College has helped the local community to get involved in events, worth around half a million pounds.

Schools across the area have also been very prolific in their support of the charity, many of which have taken Keech as their adopted charity and have made a constant flow of donations.

Stopsley High School in Luton has supported the hospice for years and raised a total of £17,468. When the school chose the hospice as their Charity of the Year in 2009, staff and students threw themselves into fundraising, holding cake and book sales, taking part in the Share a Card scheme, recycling toner cartridges and placing collection boxes in their dining room. From a non-uniform day they held in the October of that year alone, the school raised £849. Over in Markyate, Beechwood

Park has also been a loyal supporter. Having held a range of activities, including balloon races, discos, quizzes, Christmas fayres, Balls and sponsored the planting of daffodil bulbs, the school's fundraising total stands at over £140,000!

In 2010, when students at the school were encouraged to make suggestions for a charity event, Year 8 pupil, George Poole came up with the idea of producing a special photograph of the children arranged in the shape of a Beechwood tree. After discussing the idea with his Headmaster, George successfully enlisted the help of local companies, Pret-a-Portrait and EPL Skylift, to enable an aerial photograph to be taken. George said:

> *"It was extremely exciting and on the Friday afternoon, just before the half term holiday everyone came to make it happen! I was fortunate enough to be allowed to go up in the crane and was amazed by how far I could see – it was brilliant!"*

The photo turned out brilliantly and copies were then sold to families of the children featured to raise a sum of £1,216.

Acts of kindness

The story of how much support the hospice has generated from the local community over the years has truly been remarkable. Alongside the companies, schools, societies and sporting clubs, there have been church groups, local councils, media partners, youth groups, local dignitaries, charitable trusts and individuals – all of which have shown their commitment to Keech.

Across the area covered by the two hospices, there are a countless number of individuals who have, entirely off their own back, decided to give something of themselves to the charity.

Some make the odd donation in a collection box and others may turn up to volunteer for the charity every week but whether it's an act of giving time or money, no measure of support goes unappreciated.

A collection held at the airport

Ladies from the airport
get ready for the Midnight
Walk in 2009

Barnfield College students take on a charity
challenge to fundraise for the hospice in 2008

Volunteers from Wates helping with refurbishments at
the children's hospice

Luton Town Football club
cheque presentation

Beechwood Park School marking the
total they had raised by 2008

Hen and Chickens cheque presentation

In some cases, what seems a small act of kindness, can actually become something of great value to the hospice. One testament to this comes from Mike Jarman, who was a lifeguard in the hydrotherapy pool. Mike and his wife Rita remember their first contact with the hospice 20 years ago:

"We first got involved when my Mother died in 1991 and we donated the flowers from her funeral to the hospice.

"Then in 1999, just before Keech Cottage opened, we had our Ruby Wedding anniversary party and asked guests to donate to the children's hospice rather than give us presents. We raised about £800, then did the same for our Golden Wedding in 2009 and collected a similar amount.

"When you've been married for 40 years or more, you don't always need gifts, and flowers left after a funeral either wilt in the summer or die in the frost in winter, so it's pleasant to think they are enjoyed by the patients and staff."

Taking stock of all the varied and wonderful ways in which the community has got behind the hospices, Fundraising Director, Jacqui Shepherd, commented:

"While Keech has got on with caring for patients, it is the local community which has created all these very special stories of support.

"Highlighting just a few of those stories, we know there are countless thousands more.

"In my time at the hospice I have met so many remarkable people and on a daily basis I am taken aback by their ingenuity and touched by their generosity.

"Such dedication shows me, and everyone else at Keech, what an extraordinary and unique place this is.

"Thank you never seems quite enough."

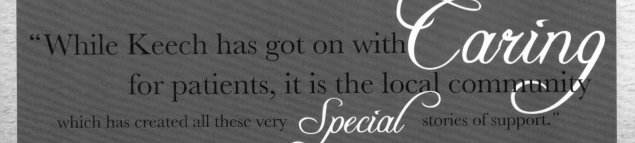

"While Keech has got on with *Caring* for patients, it is the local community which has created all these very *Special* stories of support."

Friends *of* Keech

A tale of community support

It's always a great feeling to have lots of friends – people who will help you, care for you and be there when you need them. For Keech Hospice Care it's even more than that, it's proof of the way the charity is held in the hearts of so many local people and vital to raising awareness of the work it does.

The charity has been incredibly lucky and, in its 21st year, it had a staggering 900 people volunteering, getting involved in almost every aspect of its work.

At the hospice they help with areas like housekeeping, reception duties, gardening and providing complementary therapies. Out in the community they work in the charity's shops or support fundraising – helping with community events, street collections and much more.

Keech is also very lucky to have two very special 'Friends of Keech' groups, people who have come together to help raise awareness and funds for the charity. One group covers Luton and South Bedfordshire and another works around the Bedford area.

Here's how these groups were set up, what they have done for Keech over the years and what some of their members have to say about their involvement with the charity.

When the hospice's Midsummer Show came to an end in 2005, the volunteer committee that had been involved in organising the show formed the first Friends group for the hospice (for the Luton and South Bedfordshire area).

Originally called the 'Friends of Pasque', the group was quick to find other avenues for fundraising and initially poured their collective energy into barn dances, held in New Farm in Streatley.

The farm was owned by Ross Miller, who kindly donated the whole premises for the event enabling more than 300 people to attend. In the first couple of years, these were generating £5,000-£6,000 per year. Group member since the beginning, John Adams explained:

> "You need a lot of people to fill the barn and make it worthwhile and enjoyable. Over time, we moved on to other things and we now run dances in schools in Luton and Dunstable. We have quiz nights and we are looking to move on to a Murder/Mystery night next year and we exploring other things as well. We generated around £10,000 in our best year but due to the current economic climate, we are a little below that at the moment."

The group currently has eight members: Mark Titmus (Chairman), John Adams (Secretary), Laura Randall (Treasurer), Carole Young, Jo Geiger, Ann Cassidy, Lesley O'Keefe and Judith Hawkes. Many of these are long-serving volunteers, some of whom have recently received their 20 year service volunteering badges. Each member takes responsibility for various parts of the functions they organise which now also include an annual Tea at Three party held in Barton Village Hall.

Some of the Bedford friends attending a music therapy session

As well as providing the opportunity for local people to enjoy a collective cuppa, there are usually stall holders selling garden produce, flowers, vegetables, fruit and bric-a-brac. There are games to be played and a barbecue to be enjoyed. Additionally, the group coordinates regular 60s and 70s dances with fish and chip suppers and volunteer to help with many other fundraising activities each year. They also help by spreading awareness of the charity and giving talks and presentations to groups across the local community.

Bedford friends

The Friends of Keech Bedford group were brought together by a former area fundraiser at the charity in 2006. From the start, the purpose was to raise awareness of the children's service and specifically the work it does to support families in Bedford and across central Bedfordshire. The Friends have given a significant amount of their time to the charity, helping to make presentations and collecting cheques on Keech's behalf. They have organised stalls at a range of local events such as village fairs and fêtes as well as attending larger events such as the Bedford River and Kite Festivals. Since 2008, the group have organised a very successful annual Dinner Dance. Asked about their reasons for getting involved, here is what the original members of the group had to say:

Pam Rhodes with Carolyn Heard (Mum to a child at Keech) at the Dinner Dance in 2009

"I was so impressed by the work of the charity and by the enthusiasm and energy of the committee members that I asked if I could help by joining them in their efforts. I was honoured when they accepted my offer and I have been trying to keep up ever since!"

"I joined the Friends of Keech group as my partner, Susan, was involved with Keech and felt it was a worthy cause. As a member of the Bedford Steam Engine Club, I apply for the group to have stalls at their events and I have passed my 'test' to drive Santa along in the Keech sleigh at Christmas time."
Roger Fensome

"I am a professional auctioneer and first became involved with the Friends when I was asked to conduct a fundraising sale on their behalf a few years ago. I was so impressed by the work of the charity and by the enthusiasm and energy of the committee members that I asked if I could help by joining them in their efforts. I was honoured when they accepted my offer and have been trying to keep up ever since!" David Fletcher

"I knew of Keech from my work in the Education Department of Bedfordshire County Council. While in work I collected for Keech at Christmas when we made donations in lieu of sending Christmas cards. I also organised a bucket collection at a match at Bedford Blues Rugby Club. Since joining the Friends I have given talks, collected cheques and helped with many a stall or bucket collection."
Jackie Markham

"As a member of my work's Charity committee I was made aware of Keech through a friend and we raised money via raffles and quizzes. I was so inspired by the work Keech did. I organise a raffle every year at a local Whist Drive and promote Keech wherever I can. I give talks and help on stalls at local events. Roger and I thoroughly enjoy going round with Santa on the sleigh and seeing the children's faces light up." Susan Marshall

"I originally got to know about Keech through the Bedford and District Netball League, of which I am the Chairman. When we set up the Junior League we decided to support a local charity which was children related. We decided on Keech – an easy decision once we saw the wonderful work they do. When I was Lady Captain at Bedford and County

Golf Club, I nominated Keech as my chosen charity. I then joined the Friends of Keech group in Bedford and support them in their various activities whenever I can."
Heather Nolan

"Having been a member of Round Table and Rotary Clubs for many years I have been involved in fundraising and especially enjoyed Santa's collections. I was initially involved with driving 'Smiley Sam' in Luton, through which I joined the start up of Friends of Keech. Now, among other things, I enjoy working with the sleigh, meeting a variety of interesting people in different groups and developing new skills I never thought I would need." David Whitehead

"I was initially involved with Keech through membership of Rotary. Our club had a speaker from Keech and we raised money for the hospice. In 2005 David and I walked 100 miles along the Rivers Ivel and Ouse from Baldock to Kings Lynn which raised over £2,000. Following that we became involved in the setting up of the Friends of Keech. I enjoy telling groups about the work of Keech and promoting Keech at a range of different events." Mary Whitehead

"We first heard about Keech through Three Counties Radio's Jon Gaunt a good few years ago. It was not until September 2007, when we went to a ball organised by our son's firm, Relmfield Builders, at the Sharnbrook Hotel, that we took more of an interest. When we celebrated our 40th wedding anniversary we decided to ask for donations to Keech in lieu of presents. We attended a Friends of Keech meeting to present the cheque and were invited to join." Jean and Mike Wilding

Poster advertising the Barton
Tea at Three party in 2009

Both 'Friends of Keech' groups work professionally within a structured committee and meet regularly with fundraising staff at the charity to plan and review their activities. Over the years, it has become clear that both the Luton and South Beds and the Bedford 'Friends' groups have become good friends amongst themselves. However, while they may work as close-knit groups when focused on their fundraising efforts, they are both open to new members and welcome offers of help from anyone who is willing to share their views, talents and enthusiasm. Between them, the two Friends groups have given thousands of hours and raised tens of thousands of pounds. They are a force which Keech feels privileged to have on its side.

IN THE NEWS

A journalist's eye on Keech

If there's one story guaranteed to grip our readers, it's anything hospice-related. The charity and Premier Newspapers – publishers of The Luton News, Dunstable Gazette, Herald & Post and Leighton Buzzard Observer, among others – have always enjoyed a symbiotic relationship that's mutually rewarding.

We feel proud and privileged that Keech Hospice Care trusts us enough to allow us to talk to selected patients and their families during times that can be difficult and distressing.

Many are keen to share their experiences, of how their loved ones have been cared for with compassion, skill and sensitivity, thanks to the devoted and dedicated hospice staff. And how they themselves are better able to cope with the loss of someone close because of the comfort, understanding and support available 24/7.

Their accounts are often heartbreaking, especially when a child is involved. But they are always uplifting.Take Caroline Kelly of Luton. Her second son, Declan, was born with the rare brain disorder, lissencephaly.

She dedicated her life to looking after the little boy she called 'my right hand man, my shadow, my beautiful boy.' She spoke to us to say how much the hospice had helped her.

And when Declan died in December 2008, aged just six, she contacted us again to say a huge thank you to Keech. She told us: *"They were absolutely brilliant. They loved him every bit as much as we did and we always felt he was safe when he was with them."*

Another Luton mum, Misti Brandon, has a similar story. Her youngest child, Abbie, was diagnosed with Cockayne Syndrome, a rare inherited disorder, shortly after she was born.

Misti had never heard of the hospice until she was referred with Abbie.

We interviewed her for Children's Hospice Week and she said: *"I know when Abbie's there I can relax completely. I know she'll be looked after. And if she cries, I know she'll be cuddled and loved. The hospice really is a lifeline."* Sadly Abbie lost her brave battle in 2007. But Misti was determined to put something back and joined the hospice as a volunteer.

Time and again we're told how staff always go that extra mile. Like staff nurse Angie Shipley, who'd wanted to work in a hospice all her life but only started training when she was 39. *"It was the best thing I ever did and I'm so lucky to be at Keech,"* she said. She describes palliative care as the 'Holy Grail' of nursing: "Working here is about patients, not number crunching or ticking boxes. It's about supporting the families as well as the patients. It's 100 per cent nursing care."

Angie admits it's hard when a patient dies: *"You go home and cry your eyes out but you hope you might have made their life better, their death more dignified."*

Bereavement Manager and former jazz musician, Jeff Lewcock, said the hospice wouldn't be able to operate without its volunteers: *"It always amazes me that people are prepared to give up their time to come and train."*

> "We feel like family in many ways - there for the high days and holidays, as well as all the ups and the downs, We're both here to serve the community."

Every autumn the Herald & Post runs an article requesting help for the Hospice at Home service. The paper interviews a cross-section of volunteers about why they do it and what they get out of it.

Stalwart Carole Spalding of Round Green, who's been with the service 20 years, joked she was *"hanging on for the gold watch."* On a more serious note, she added: "I just like all the different people – they're all so inspiring." Lead Coordinator, Elaine Foster, said: "The H&P appeal always has a fantastic response. We're inundated with people who want to sign up for our Course of Preparation." Premier Newspapers also carries stories of the hospice's fundraising activities - like the Midnight Walk and Santa Fun Run – and all the other ingenious ideas staff and supporters think up to swell the coffers. Visually-impaired IT boffin Dave Birtwhistle of Ennismore Green raised more than £1,800 by doing a parachute jump. The father-of-two suffers from a condition called Drusen (calcification of the optic nerve fibres).

But that didn't stop his high flying adventure. He described it as *"going from abject terror to total exhilaration in two seconds flat."* He wanted to raise money because he hates to think of children suffering and dying, but he's also horrified that the hospice relies on the local community for so much of its income.

Our own Steve Nolan, senior reporter on the Luton News, has taken part in three charity challenges – the inaugural firewalk in 2009, a skydive in 2010 and the more recent 'Jail and Bail' where he was incarcerated with some of the town's movers and shakers.

He persuaded family, friends and colleagues to part with a creditable £600 to release him from his Mall 'cell.'

We also report on the personalities who are either ambassadors for the charity or who find the time to front high profile activities or visit its patients. Stars of sport, stage and screen like race ace Lewis Hamilton, King of the ring Billy Schwer and Luton's own spin ball wizard, Monty Panesar. Then there's the BBC's Pam Rhodes and Billy Byrne as well as Jake Humphrey, Esther Rantzen and super chef Jean-Christophe Novelli, who donated his £10,000 winnings from Celebrity Mr and Mrs to the hospice.

The Luton News
through thick…

…and through thin,

The papers cover news events such as major lottery wins, the launch of the Walk of Life, the rebranding in 2009 and the opening of the new in-patient unit in 2010. But we're also here to let our readers know when times are tough, as they were last year when the country was in recession and the charity faced redundancies.

We feel like family in many ways – there for the high days and holidays, as well as all the ups and the downs. We're both here to serve the community. We pick up and retain readers by reporting what's happening at the hospice. And by highlighting how the service is there for the people who need it, we raise awareness of its unique place in our society and encourage vital fundraising to ensure its survival.

Bev Creagh (Feature writer, Premier Newspapers)

Chapter Thirteen

Celebration time

"You have helped us to cope through one of the worst times in our lives...Your care and compassion, ability to listen, support and just 'being there' have meant so much to us..."

Some say the life-line of an organisation is much like that of a person. It's born in a rather fledgling state, finds its feet during the early years and then grows, develops and builds in confidence over time – sometimes at quite alarming rates!

In the same way that we celebrate the birth of a child and then wonder where the time has gone when they reach their 1st birthday and every birthday thereafter, Keech Hospice Care has met each anniversary with that similar sense of surprise and pride.

A very special Year...

The year 2001 proved a very special year for the charity. As it celebrated ten years of providing care for local adults, it was also the very first birthday of Keech Cottage Children's Hospice.

The celebrations reported in the hospice's own newsletter, The Pasque News

community had rallied behind the children's hospice came when BBC Three Counties and Luton North Rotary combined forces to donate two minibuses to the hospice. These were valuable additions which enabled the care team to widen the net for the children in their care. They could now take them safely out on trips to the shops, cinema, parks and to local attractions such as Woodside Animal Farm.

The 10th year and 1st year anniversaries were jointly celebrated with a wonderful birthday cake featuring the names of both hospice services, Keech and Pasque, as well as their corresponding emblems, the butterfly and the Pasque flower.

Over the next decade the charity celebrated various anniversaries in the life of its children's and adult service. Here are some of those milestones.

During the first ten years, the hospice had helped thousands of adult patients from across Luton and South Bedfordshire to lead an acceptable, purposeful and fulfilling life and to achieve a dignified death. At the time, the daughter of one hospice patient commented:

"You have helped us to cope through one of the worst times in our lives… Your care and compassion, ability to listen, support and just 'being there' have meant so much to us… thank you so much for everything."

The first year of the children's hospice had proven to be an exciting time, during which it had welcomed in a new team of nurses and carers, made contact with around 120 families who needed specialist care for their child and received wonderful support from across the community. Just one example of the way the

The two hospice's birthday celebrations, as reported in one of the local newspapers

Children's hospice turns 5

In 2005, Keech Cottage Children's Hospice proudly announced its 5th birthday with a 'We are 5' badge adorned to its newsletters, website, all correspondence and everything else it could find.

The achievements of the past five years were rightly celebrated. In that time the numbers of children and families supported had more than doubled to 250 and, with funding from the Big Lottery Fund, the community nursing service had been substantially extended. A team of eleven children's nurses, nursery nurses and carers were now working in the homes of families across Bedfordshire and Hertfordshire.

Amidst the celebrations there was, as always, the challenge to raise the funds needed to run the children's service, which at the time was a sum of £1.8 million a year. With the prospect of Big Lottery Fund money coming to an end the following year, fundraisers at the charity faced the need to find alternative sources of income to ensure the future of its children's community service. None of this stopped the celebrations from going ahead but many were simply given a bit of a fundraising edge!

During the course of its birthday year, the charity ran various campaigns based around the number five to encourage people in the community to get involved in fundraising and held a number of special events.

One such event took place on 6th May, when the Mayor of St Albans, Councillor Gordon Myland, and Mayoress, Pat Garrard hosted a spectacular May Ball for the charity. Held at Sopwell House Hotel, guests were treated to a line-up featuring fireworks, live bands, fantastic prizes and celebrity guest speaker, Gillian Taylforth (of Eastenders and Footballers Wives fame).

Taking a step away from the fundraising, the magnificent setting of St Albans Cathedral provided the backdrop for a very moving 'Service of Celebration', held on 5th June. Over 300 people joined the service which included readings, prayers and a performance from Pasque Harmony. Throughout, there was barely a dry eye to be seen as everyone came together to both celebrate the fifth birthday and remember the lives of the children who had been helped by Keech over the previous five years. Leading the congregation's reflections on five main themes of joy, love, loss, life and hope during the service was Chief Executive at the time, John Quill. He spoke about the joy of becoming a parent; the love that is there between a parent and child; the pain when a family faces the premature loss of their child; the way those families and others can carry on with their lives; and how life can and does get better because of an enduring spirit of hope.

Speaking after the service, he said:

"I'm really pleased with the day, the feeling in the Abbey as we went from joy to sorrow and back to joy, and the many positive comments we received about the service and our work. We have worked with many children and their families over the last five years and this service gave us all the opportunity to remember their short but incredibly important lives."

Keech Cottage's Fifth birthday badge

Pasque Harmony at the Service of Celebration, St Albans Cathedral in 2005

A Royal visit

"She was quick to get down on her knees for an impromptu sing-a-long with the children."

The Countess of Wessex with staff and families at Keech

The pinnacle of Keech's 5th birthday celebrations came when staff and families at the children's hospice welcomed HRH the Countess of Wessex to the children's hospice on 26th September 2005. Much to the concern of her aides, the Countess stayed well beyond her allotted time as she toured the facilities and witnessed some of the day-to-day activities at the children's hospice.

Throughout her visit, the Countess took the time to speak with many of the children and their families and to staff and volunteers. Joining the 'Tots and Toys' parent and toddler group that was taking place that day, she was quick to get down on her knees for an impromptu sing-a-long with the children!

Chief Executive, John Quill, spoke for everyone when he commented after the event:

"The Countess is known to be a keen supporter of children's hospices and her genuine interest really came through during her visit. This was an important event for us, as it highlights and confirms the need for our service and recognises the care that we give to our children and their families. Showing her around I felt very proud of everything we do here."

" I felt *Very proud* of everything we do here. "

The Countess of Wessex with staff
and families at Keech

15 years
adult care

June 2006 saw the charity celebrating again, this time to commemorate 15 years of care at the adult hospice.

To mark the occasion, over 100 guests joined staff and volunteers at an anniversary tea party held in the hospice gardens, in a location where the current adult in-patient unit now stands. Tony Bignell, a relative of a hospice patient, sang for the crowd and the sun shone over what was a wonderful afternoon filled with a mixture of tears and laughter as people recalled their memorable times at the hospice.

In a poignant moment of reflection, family members of past patients were asked to release 15 balloons, one for each year the adult hospice had been open. For many, the highlight of the afternoon were two personal tributes to the charity, one made by Isabel Rigby whose daughter Erin died at Keech Cottage and another by Steve Kay whose wife, Lin died in the adult unit.

During the party, the charity also took the opportunity to congratulate its lucky 15th Anniversary Lottery winner, Peter Hill, who scooped a top prize which had been doubled to £2000 especially for the occasion. It was a prize worth giving as the special draw raised a record £43,135 for the charity.

Mr Hill, who immediately donated £200 back to the hospice, was delighted with his win:

"Winning came as a big shock but a very nice one! My wife and I have played the lottery for two years by standing order and we feel very pleased to be regularly supporting such a good cause in the community."

Scenes from the 15th Anniversary tea party

Singer, Tony Bignall

Lottery winner Peter Hill receiving his cheque

Ten in 2010

In 2010, the charity, now renamed as 'Keech Hospice Care', took time to commemorate the fact that ten years had gone by since the opening of the children's hospice.

Keech was still the only children's hospice service across Bedfordshire and Hertfordshire and since 2007 has extended its service to families living in Milton Keynes. There was now a team of 25 children's nurses, nursery nurses and carers working at the hospice and a further 14 out in the community.

That included four members of a 'Closer to Home' team, a new service that had been launched in 2008 to pick up the respite needs of children and families in Bedfordshire and Luton.

Over the years many developments in care had been made, from the creation of a 'Tots n Toys' playgroup for pre-school age children to peer group sessions for teenage girls and boys, that once again Keech felt it a worthy landmark to celebrate.

So, on 29th March 2010, children, families, staff and guests gathered for an afternoon of magic, face painting, 'clowning' around and crafts at the hospice. Special guests and original benefactors of the hospice, Dennis and Shirley Keech, cut the birthday cake – helped by Keech patient, Ellie Picton, and her mum, Angie. Amongst the guests was Phillip Knight, whose 6 year-old daughter had Congenital Myotonic Dystrophy and needed constant care and attention. Phillip, from Milton Keynes, explained what Keech meant to their lives:

"Abigail's condition can deteriorate very quickly and we can take her to Keech even at the last minute. When she goes to the hospice, we have time to recharge our batteries and relax. All the family are able to visit whenever they want and Abigail gets one-to-one care, 24-hours a day. She always sleeps so well when she stays there as they have so many activities to keep her occupied, when elsewhere she can't always do the things normal children do. Coming today is like being with our extended family. It's so nice to have friends who are in the same position as us – we're all in the same boat and so lucky to have the support of Keech."

Mike Keel, who has been with the children's hospice from the start and was appointed Chief Executive at the charity in 2011, gave his thoughts on the occasion:

"Today, we look back on a decade of providing expert care for local children and look forward to another ten years of providing that care to all who need it. We are proud of all of the work we have done over the years but there is always more to be done and we have quite significant aspirations for the future. Meanwhile, none of what we've done would have been possible without the continuous backing of our community and I hope everyone shares our sense of achievement with us in our tenth year."

Keech comes of age

As Keech Hospice Care enters its 21st year of providing specialist palliative care, in some ways the hospice itself is barely recognisable from how it first began back in 1991. Along the way there have been new buildings, new services, new facilities and new faces in the team.

But, time and time again, the charity is fortunate to hear the same thing from people who visit either of the hospices – the view that, throughout its history, what remains steadfast is the enthusiasm and dedication of everyone who works there and the wonderful atmosphere you feel when you walk through the doors.

The Lord Lieutenant for Bedfordshire, Sir Samuel Whitbread, most recently expressed this view when he visited the hospice for the opening of its newly extended and refurbished day hospice. Looking around, he commented:

> *"I've been here at Keech many times over the last 21 years and every time I see something different. What is always the same though is the enthusiasm and the happy smiling faces of all the staff."*

"...Throughout its history, what remains steadfast is the enthusiasm and dedication of everyone who works there and the *Wonderful* atmosphere you feel when you walk through the doors."

Clowning around at the party

The Knight family

Cutting the cake

Weddings At the hos

"If anyone had told me that I would ever cry with joy at the news of a *Loved one* going into a hospice, I wouldn't have believed them, but cry I did. I was desperate for someone to help him..."

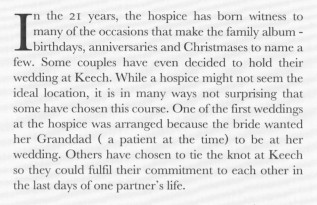

In the 21 years, the hospice has born witness to many of the occasions that make the family album - birthdays, anniversaries and Christmases to name a few. Some couples have even decided to hold their wedding at Keech. While a hospice might not seem the ideal location, it is in many ways not surprising that some have chosen this course. One of the first weddings at the hospice was arranged because the bride wanted her Granddad (a patient at the time) to be at her wedding. Others have chosen to tie the knot at Keech so they could fulfil their commitment to each other in the last days of one partner's life.

Colin Chapman and his fiancé at the time, Tina Dodge chose to do this in August 2001. Colin had been admitted from the Luton and Dunstable Hospital very seriously ill. When the couple expressed their wish to be married, the adult hospice care team rallied to the challenge. Given that there was a lot to organise within a few hours the Superintendent Register for Bedfordshire was asked what was the latest time they could conduct such a ceremony. The reply came that under the circumstances they could come day or night!

Sarah and Rob Bates married at Keech in October 2007, just days before Rob lost his battle with cancer. Here she tells her story of love, loss and new friends.

When Rob and I met, I was struck by his huge smile and warm personality. Our relationship grew quickly and became very strong. We felt that we were soul mates and meant to be together. Rob already had two children but, as time went on, we decided to have a family of our own, and so Daisy was born in 2005. Sadly, Daisy and her Daddy were together for such a short period of time. Rob first mentioned discomfort in his chest in October 2006. The following January, an MRI scan showed a collapsed vertebrae, most probably caused by cancer. What a terrifying word that is. Rob was admitted into hospital for surgery to repair his spine, but this was abandoned due to haemorrhaging. Unfortunately he was never well enough again for the surgery to go ahead. We were told the cancer Rob had, Multiple Myeloma, was incurable, but could be controlled with treatment.

pice

"Perfect Wedding..."

Rob and Sarah on their wedding day

In-patient Unit Wedding Bells

"Rob was so handsome and it was the easiest thing in the world to say 'I do'. he made me the

Happiest Woman

alive that day and I like to think that I made him the happiest man. He shared my world for three more days."

Sarah Bates with sculpture in memory of Rob

"Rob responded well..."

Rob responded well to chemotherapy and started to feel better. He was able to get up with the aid of a back brace and we felt 'lucky' that we had been given this opportunity to realise what was really important in life. We grabbed it with both hands.

These happy times were relatively short-lived, as Rob's cancer proved extremely aggressive and eventually, the treatment options ran out. Whilst Rob was in the Luton and Dunstable Hospital for pain control, the Macmillan Nurse and a doctor from Pasque visited us to discuss moving to the hospice. If anyone had told me that I would ever cry with joy at the news of a loved one going into a hospice, I wouldn't have believed them, but cry I did. I was desperate for someone to help him.

We were received into the loving care of the wonderful hospice staff and a bed was found for me so we could spend this precious time together. After caring for Rob at home, having that responsibility removed from my shoulders meant we could just be a couple again. We talked, laughed and cried and I helped him in every way I could, but I knew there was always someone to help with any problems. Rob knew that, whatever time he had left, he would not be in pain any more. What a relief that was.

Before Rob's illness, we were planning to marry but, of course, this had been forgotten. It was a chance comment made during our admission that the idea of a hospice wedding was first mentioned. While we had dreamed of our special day in a remote castle, we actually had the perfect wedding, at Rob's bedside in the hospice.

We had flowers, champagne, a beautiful cake and a harpist (Anna, the music therapist). Our guests were our new friends from the hospice, and nurses, Kim and Mandy, were our beautiful bridesmaids and witnesses. Rob was so handsome and it was the easiest thing in the world to say 'I do'. He made me the happiest woman alive that day and I like to think that I made him the happiest man. He shared my world for three more days.

Letting go is the last thing I want to do but allowing myself to release my grip on Rob doesn't mean I will forget him or love him any less. Daisy knows her Daddy is with the moon and stars, and when she recently asked me "does the moon have windows Mummy?" I answered: "Yes, the stars." Now, we look at them together and imagine Rob, Daddy, on his journey.

Sarah Bates,
wife to Rob

Chapter Fourteen

An era of modernisation

If you spend months or even years working on plans to extend your home, it's so often the case that once the major work has been done, you realise your existing rooms have been neglected but could be much improved.

A similar thing happened when the building of Keech Cottage Children's Hospice came to an end. As the children's hospice opened in a blaze of glory, the potential of just what could be achieved came to be realised and so, eyes at the charity turned to what could enhance the site as a whole.

"The £500,000 pledge from the government is brilliant news. We've been aiming to re-develop the adult hospice for some time..."

By the time the adult hospice was celebrating its 15th anniversary in 2006, the need to modernise its buildings and facilities became more significant. Over the years, much had changed. There were new techniques and equipment being used in palliative care; new standards had been issued by the National Institute for Clinical Excellence; and legislation had changed too, for instance with new rules about mixed gender wards.

It was clear that major changes were needed to properly meet the needs of patients and their families. The Board of Trustees began to look at the options in terms of what was necessary and what was desirable while also assessing the scale of the work that would be involved in achieving any of those things.

The key areas for improvement were identified as the adult In-patient Unit, Day Hospice, the laundry areas, kitchen and reception.

However, as always, funding was the biggest issue. With the costs of running the charity rising and a difficult few years for fundraising, getting started on a major building programme that could cost up to £2.65 million seemed to be a pipedream.

Then, in 2007, the charity got the breakthrough it needed when it was awarded a grant of £500,000 from the Department of Health.

The award was part of a government grant programme worth £40 million, designed to help hospices make physical improvements to their buildings and facilities.

Set alongside the idea that the hospice could re-allocate rooms in its existing unit for other work which could be commissioned by local healthcare authorities, the grant heralded the start of major works to rebuild rather than refurbish the adult In-patient Unit.

Chief Executive at the time, John Quill expressed his delight at the news:

One of the architect's drawings

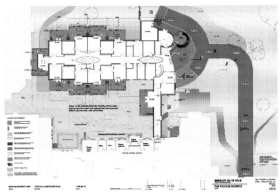

"The £500,000 pledge from the government is brilliant news. We've been aiming to re-develop the adult hospice for some time in order to properly meet the needs of our patients and modern standards in care. But, while we've been facing yearly income shortfalls, the prospect of moving forward with those plans has seemed a distant vision. There is still a lot of work to do to raise the full amount required but the arrival of this grant has steered the way for us to progress our plans."

With the addition of another £600,000 pledged from private donors who wanted to support the project and fundraisers making plans to raise the rest, the project was given the green light.

In the autumn of 2007, the hospice officially unveiled its plans to rebuild its In-patient Unit with eight new en-suite bedrooms, a new reception area, nurse base, storage rooms, drug control areas, quiet spaces for patients and their guests and a special room designed to allow bereaved families to spend some last moments with their loved one.

Director of Nursing at the time, Mike Keel, explained how important such improvements were for the hospice and its patients:

> *"We desperately need to keep pace with all the changes that have taken place over the last few years to create an adult hospice service fit for the 21st century. Put simply, our existing In-patient Unit was not designed to accommodate the facilities and equipment we now need and it no longer provides the special environment required to care for the more dependent and sick patients we are seeing today. Our patients deserve the best and it's our aim to give them precisely that."*

Building the new adult In-patient Unit

It took a few more months for building work to get underway, but on 29th April 2008, the first turf was officially 'turned' by the High Sheriff of Bedfordshire, Nazir Jessa.

Work to clear the land was then quickly carried out by a small team of Irishmen, lead by local developer Don Wall. The men gave their time, along with their plant and machinery, for free at an estimated value of £25,000. Nine years previously, Don and his team had cleared the land for the children's hospice, also free of charge.

With the site cleared, the building work commenced and despite a few snow-related delays during the winter, most of the work went to schedule. The builders handed back the keys to the building in March 2009, after which there came a final period of arranging fittings and furnishings for the unit.

Nurse, Kim Theobald explained how that task sounded a lot simpler than it proved:

> *"We re-used as much as we could from the old unit but couldn't strip it bare because of plans to use those rooms in other ways. So we still had quite a large list to get through with everything on it from drug cupboards to waste bins. There was also much to consider with regards to balancing what we needed for medical care and how to ensure furnishings supported our infection control measures with what would make our patients and their families feel comfortable and at ease."*

Keeping the money coming in

While the new unit was taking shape, the charity's fundraisers had been working tirelessly to raise the final £1 million needed to complete the project, all while maintaining the core income needed to run both hospice services.

Soon after the land had been cleared, the charity launched a public campaign called 'Building for Better Care'. The appeal, which was repeatedly featured in local newspapers, The Luton News and Dunstable Gazette, got off to a great start with a donation of £6,000 from Kent Retired Employees Association. By its third month, the appeal was boosted again when thousands of local people made donations amounting to a total of £43,000 and then another charitable foundation made a pledge of £100,000.

In the months ahead, fundraising took every turn imaginable, from local people taking part in a sponsored Firewalk (braving 20ft of hot coals barefoot) to signing tiles to go on the roof. The charity also launched its 'Walk of Life', a special pathway laid close the new unit. In return for a donation, supporters chose their own inscription for one of the stones. The messages we see there today feature a heart-warming mix of those remembering loved ones alongside simple messages of goodwill and support for the charity.

1st week of construction

Arriva buses help with promotion

10th week of construction

Taking shape

On Monday 9th November 2009, patient care at the adult hospice was finally transformed when the new In-patient Unit was officially opened by broadcaster, Esther Rantzen.

As well as cutting the ribbon across the unit, Esther spent time with some of the first patients and their families to use the unit and on behalf of the charity, gave each one a boxed crystal heart memento.

Speaking on the occasion, she said:

"This is a very happy place – an exceptional combination of vision and hard work, a dream come true. It has the most wonderful atmosphere and everyone here is dedicated to quality of life. There is so much skill and care and the staff are all patient-oriented."

Trustees, patrons, major donors, staff, volunteers, representatives from charitable trusts that had supported the project and those involved in the design and build of the unit were also at the opening to witness this important development in local adult hospice care.

And so, from then onwards, patients staying at the hospice benefited from everything the new unit had to offer – bigger bedrooms with individually controlled heating, lighting and ventilation; private Jacuzzi bathing facilities; tranquil areas inside and out; sitting and kitchen areas for their families to use at their leisure; ceiling hoists to help them to move around more easily and with dignity and much more.

"This is a very happy place - an exceptional combination of vision and hard work, a dream come true. It has the most wonderful atmosphere and everyone here is dedicated to quality of life. There is so much skill and care and the staff are all patient-oriented."

A
Dream
comes true

(Top to bottom)
Entrance
Reception area
Bedroom
Esther Rantzen opens the new unit in 2009

"It's a transformation and I feel at *Home* here."

One of the first patients to move into the unit was Daphne Bowers, who had previously been staying in the older unit for help with the pain caused by her condition. Sadly, Daphne died a few weeks after the opening, but at the time she said:

"When I first saw the new unit, I fell in love with it! It is so modern and comfortable and I have a nice view of the patio and gardens. I have been for a bath in the en-suite. It was so easy using the hoist and the nurses are so great. It's a transformation and I feel at home here, with my photos on the notice board and the drawers full of my things."

Shirley Gadsden, Senior Sister for the adult hospice, spoke of the benefits seen by the nursing team:

"The team has settled in well, as have our patients. The new equipment is making the day-to-day care we provide easier and more comfortable for patients and our infection control is at a very high standard. We would like to thank everyone who has supported the new build – it means a great deal to all of us, especially the families we care for."

A look at day care

At the hospice, once you finish working on one project, another one seems to loom. At Keech, the opening of its adult In-patient Unit was certainly something to celebrate but it also signalled the time had come for attention to be turned to the other areas it wanted to improve and modernise.

However, with the British economy in a particularly sorry state and many local people finding it a struggle to keep up with the financial needs of their own household, Keech knew it couldn't ask its community to help more than it was already doing.

Then in 2010, the charity's hopes for further modernisation seemed possible once more as the Department of Health announced the second phase of its £40 million capital grant programme for hospices.

Health Secretary, Andrew Lansley, said:

"Hospices make an immense contribution in providing compassionate, quality care for people at the end of life. This is why the £40 million hospice capital grant scheme was so vital. I am delighted about the major improvements this funding has made possible at hospices across England."

Luckily, Keech Hospice Care was one of 116 hospices across England to be awarded a grant, this time to the value of £200,000. Not knowing when the next opportunity of such funding might be available, Keech decided that the changes it wanted to make to its Day Hospice should be made a priority. Combined with further grants from several charitable trusts, there was enough in the pot to do a little more and so the laundry area was also included in the plan.

This was chosen ahead of upgrading the reception and dining areas because combining the hospice's two laundries into one would save the charity money in the longer term.

In just five months, during which day care was moved temporarily into what had previously been used as conference rooms, the work was completed. Re-opening on 23rd May 2011, the new day unit, now named 'The Keech Palliative Care Centre' had been significantly expanded.

The more spacious areas had been designed with wheelchairs in mind and there were new dedicated spaces for art therapy, multi-faith facilities, private consulting rooms, much improved toilet and bathroom facilities, a new family room and quiet areas for patients and carers to relax. In addition to all of this, the hospice's laundry areas had been combined and refurbished and the whole area had been redecorated throughout, giving it a much more modern and fresh feel.

The refurbishment and opening of the newly refurbished Keech Palliative Care Centre

Adult Services Manager, Elaine Tolliday spoke about the impact she felt these changes would have in the months and years ahead:

"Our new day care centre has been designed in such a way that we can use it much more effectively for the combination of group activities and individual patient support that we offer.

"However, the physical changes are only part of the story. Our aim has been to provide an environment where we can widen the range of services we offer to significantly more patients and their carers. We'll continue to run our established day service but will also be providing more drop-in sessions and out-patient clinics. We're also creating a games area that will help us to support young people as they start to outgrow our children's hospice and in the near future we also hope to set up specific clinics that will help our patients with issues such as breathlessness and fatigue management.

"All in all, this new development helps us to better support our patients in a way that suits their different needs and lifestyles."

An official re-opening was attended by a wealth of local dignitaries, trustees and long-term supporters of the hospice including Sir Samuel Whitbread and Dr Wink White. To mark the occasion, Chief Executive, Mike Keel asked one of the nurses, Sybil Amassy-Wade, to cut the official ribbon. Addressing both supporters and the proud team at Keech he spoke of the continued commitment the charity has made to improving care:

"This latest development at the hospice is just part of a long-term programme of improvements which we have undertaken in recent years and which we'll continue to work on in the years ahead. Our focus is always to do everything we can to provide quality care to more local people while working with the resources we have. I believe that this exciting project has taken us another step forward in achieving this."

Green fingers

For around three years after the adult hospice opened, the grounds were simply laid out to grass with a few specimen trees and some donated rose beds. There was a gravel pathway around the building but most of the garden was inaccessible to wheelchairs. This was all to change from 1995 onwards when volunteer, Judy Hawkes, was asked to design and landscape the whole site. Up until that time, Judy and a few other volunteers had been helping to keep the perimeter around the building tidy but the challenge of designing the entire garden was something she threw herself into. Judy said:

"It was a bit daunting but also exciting. Once the design was finalised and approved by the trustees, the work began. We didn't have much equipment in those days – no ride-on mowers or trailers. So we dug up the turf by hand and shifted it in wheelbarrows!"

The first big feature to be developed was the 'Quiet Garden' which was to become the focal point of the whole garden. This tranquil area featured pathways, fragrant flowerbeds, sculptures and secluded seating areas. The plants and flowers took two or three years to mature but once the hedge encircling the garden reached head height it became a private space much loved by many people. A garden which saw happiness and laughter, sadness and tears but was always a place of peace. Having taken an R.H.S garden course at Barnfield College, Judy roped in fellow student, Lesley O'Keeffe to help. Over the next fifteen years the pair, along with a growing team of volunteers, changed the topography around the hospice entirely.

Other achievements for the gardening team, involved landscaping the gardens around the day hospice building, the nurturing of an orchard and woodland areas and years of growing and selling produce from greenhouses which helped to ensure the gardens became self-sufficient.

"A garden which saw happiness and

laughter...

sadness and tears but was always a place of peace.

(Top) Luton in Bloom
(Bottom) Official opening of greenfingers garden

In the beginning, the gardens were such a large feature of the hospice but as each building stage came about (the children's hospice and the new adult unit) so too did a lot of re-landscaping for the gardens. The team of volunteers always rallied round and restored harmony to the garden. The last development, the new adult unit, saddened the team as a large part of the garden was lost, including the 'Quiet Garden' of which they were so proud. However, many would agree that it has been an incredibly rewarding experience to see how people have enjoyed the garden.

There have always been lots of people in the garden – out for a stroll, to have lunch or simply to sit and enjoy. Judy remembers the words of one lady who she came across sitting in the garden – "If heaven is like this, I'm ready to go any time".

Judy and Lesley recall many special moments throughout their time at the charity, one of which was the first 'Garden Open Day', to which several hundred visitors came. It was held shortly after the opening of the children's hospice and the gardeners and housekeepers worked together on stalls in the garden selling plants, teas and cakes. It was a very rewarding and enjoyable day which raised £2,000 and exceeded all expectation.

Another special time came in 2,000 when unbeknown to the garden team, John Maddox entered the hospice gardens in the 'Luton in Bloom' competition where they won the Mayor's Cup – the top award. The following year, the gardens won first prize in the Community Gardens category and the year after they won again, this time in a new category for Environmental Landscaping.

Judy and Lesley, who both still volunteer at the hospice today, summed up:

"We have had some really happy times and formed some firm friendships. We have seen many volunteers come and go over the years but ultimately we have all played an important part in continual garden development and maintenance and long may it continue!"

"If *heaven* is like this, I'm ready to go any time."

Chapter Fifteen

Evolving care

> "The hospice world is regarded by some as one of the greatest social innovations of the last 100 years"

When the first modern hospice, St Christopher's, opened in south London in 1967, its principles of excellent clinical care, education and research inspired many to follow suit, leading to a somewhat rapid phase of hospice development across the UK and globally.

Within ten years, it became accepted that hospice care could be practised in many settings including specialist in-patient units, home-care and day-care services. Year 1982 brought about a further development when a friendship between Sister Frances Dominica and the family of a seriously ill little girl called Helen, lead to the founding of the first children's hospice in the UK, Helen House in Oxfordshire.

Today, hospice care for both adults and children has grown into a worldwide movement that has radically changed the way we approach death and dying. It is regarded by some as one of the greatest social innovations of the last hundred years.

Within its own 21 year lifespan, Keech Hospice Care has grown alongside the wider hospice movement and undergone many a transformation. Taking an aerial view, one would have witnessed the physical expansion of the buildings. Looking at things on paper, one might notice more the changes to the organisation's name over the years. But, head deeper into the organisation and, from within the thousands of patients' stories, from the managerial discussions and from the expertise within the care team, you'll find the thing that keeps Keech going today – the driving force to transform the experience of death and dying. To maintain this role, the care services offered at Keech have quite naturally evolved to take account of clinical developments, to meet the changing needs of patients and to respond to latest thinking in palliative care.

Changing status

One of the first times the organisation recognised a real need to evolve came as early as 1994. Having been open for three years, the adult hospice had a team of part-time GPs but none of these, or any of the nursing team, had any specialist palliative care qualifications. And, although the hospice had close relationships with some senior physicians at the Luton and Dunstable Hospital (in particular the Senior Chest Physician, Dr David Siegler), there was little liaison with the Oncology Department at a specialist level.

When he arrived in 1994, General Manager, Martin Johnson described the need to improve the hospice's clinical reputation as a specialist palliative care service as one of the biggest challenges confronting the charity at that time:

> *"Out in the wider world, as things stood we couldn't have been classified as a specialist palliative care service. In the early days, the hospice matron had cultivated a very holistic approach and that had brought some great benefits for our patients but once we'd begun to expand we had to concentrate on getting proper medical cover."*

To kick off the process, medical support at the hospice came under the clinical supervision of Dr David Siegler. Given the role of Honorary Medical Director, Dr Siegler worked in this capacity up until 1997 when the new Medical Director, Dr Elizabeth Horak, was appointed. With an

MD and PhD in cancer research, Dr Horak was passionate about developing palliative medicine within the hospice. Around the same time, two or three of the senior nurses were working on getting their specialist qualifications. By 1998, as more specialist medical cover at the hospice had advanced, so too had the move by the hospice to attain greater clinical credibility.

Today, the hospice has a team of seven doctors working various hours across both hospices. Each brings substantial experience to the charity of palliative care or paediatrics.

But reputation within the medical field was not the only thing to affect the services provided at the hospice. With a proportion (currently around 25%) of its funding coming from statutory sources, the two hospices have always had to undertake serious negotiations with the local healthcare authorities and social services, many of which have proved fundamental to the changes that took place.

From the time that John Quill took over as Chief Executive in 2000, and with two hospice services to fund, discussions with local authorities had to take two different turns. For the adult hospice, much of the dialogue was held in relation to the Cancer Network (although not all patients had cancer) and the hospice had to constantly demonstrate that it was caring for the 'right sort' of patients. On the whole this was fairly straightforward because the adult hospice patients largely fell into a similar mould. By the time they got to the hospice, most were not expected to live very long and the majority were older rather than younger. However, John remembers things were not so clear-cut for the children's hospice:

"It became very clear that, for the children's hospice, things were actually very complex. I was being told about children who were close to death but who went on to live longer, and children who were expected to live a long time suddenly dying. What they had in common was that they were very seriously ill (complex is indeed the word) and had a prognosis that they wouldn't live to old age. But how long they had to live was often uncertain, not least because medical support was changing all the time and changing things for many of them."

During the early 'noughties', this complexity caused John, Mike Keel and the management team at the hospice to take a thorough look at the services provided. John commented:

"There is a 'traditional' and I have to say rather 'precious' approach to children's hospice care that is about providing whatever a family with a dying child wants. But, apart from the fact that this just isn't possible with the resources available, it wasn't in my opinion the right approach. Children with a complex condition are on a journey – they aren't necessarily ill in the same way all the time. As such, they and their families need different support at different

times. The hospice has to offer the best support it can – at the right time and in the right place, often at home through the community team. So it wasn't about 'our' children (a phrase some hospices like to use) but about being available for any children who needed our particular expertise."

This shift in thinking lead to two major, and in a way contradictory, changes.

The first came about early in 2004 when Appledore, a respite home for children with various health and social care needs from Luton and Bedfordshire, had to close quite suddenly.

John negotiated a contract with local social services for Keech to offer a certain number of bed nights for some of the children who had complex health needs. He remembers:

"This opened up a new income stream at a time when it was very much needed. But more importantly, it allowed us to demonstrate to statutory colleagues, and to families, that we were willing to be helpful and make the best use of our facilities for a range of children, including those who didn't fit the 'traditional' hospice definition because they weren't dying in the near future.

"But they were just as ill, at least some of the time, as many of the children who were expected to die quite soon, and I was clear it was entirely appropriate for Keech to be available for them. In many ways this was the beginning of a change in the approach of the children's hospice. It was a shift from being a place only for children with terminal illnesses to providing care for children with complex conditions that may not necessarily be immediately life-threatening but were almost inevitably life-limiting."

Up until this same period in time, Keech Cottage had been offering families known to the hospice pre-bookable respite care.

However, this had begun to cause some difficulties, for instance at times when a very sick child urgently needed a bed at the hospice but none was available because of children staying in for respite care.

As a result, the management team took the difficult decision to stop pre-booked respite care. John said:

"It was hard because, by this time, we had quite a large number of families who had been benefiting from planned breaks, but we couldn't continue with a situation where some of the very sickest children were being turned away, or they were coming in and families, who had perhaps booked a holiday, were being let down. It was a case of making sure families could always access our services when they really needed us. The situation had to be handled sensitively and there was certainly some winning of hearts and minds to be done. We didn't say the children couldn't ever come for short breaks, just that this couldn't be booked months in advance."

In some ways, this appeared contradictory with the deal the charity had made with regards to the Appledore children and families, but Sharon Kelly, the Children's Service Social Worker, managed the situation in a way that ensured the hospice could deliver its contract for these children without blocking beds for others.

Whilst the practicalities of these decisions panned out at Keech, John remembers the shift was not immediately held in high regard within the children's hospice world or welcomed by all of the local families who used the hospice.

"We held a meeting with parents, some with children who were seriously ill right then, and some with children who weren't so ill but who had been receiving pre-booked respite. It was a hard meeting, but eventually the parents heard what was being said and, more importantly, heard each other and saw that there needed to be a change."

Meanwhile, the adult service, which had been founded as a sort of 'cottage hospice' primarily providing respite for people

John Quill

who were dying and their families, was becoming an increasingly specialist service which could no longer take patients for long periods of respite. As with the children's work, this was a better fit with partners in the wider provision of healthcare services and again the principle was to make sure the right patients got the right care at the right time and place. Once more, this was an approach that was not entirely popular, particularly among those who had been involved in founding the hospice. However, John and his team were clear that this was the best way forward and he was glad to have the support of trustees. From the point of view of the patients, while the hospice services might have been more focussed, they got the same caring approach they had always had.

> "It wasn't about 'our' children (a phrase some hospices like to use) but about being available for any children who needed our particular expertise."

A *Shoulder* to lean on

Whilst the charity's status among the medical profession and relationships with statutory partners clearly influenced some of its decisions, not every story of the two hospices' evolving care has been influenced in this way. Many aspects of the care that Keech provides today came about due to expert opinion or innovations from within both the wider field of palliative care and the care team at Keech itself. One area which evolved in this way was the support and therapeutic services offered to patients and families at both hospices. A noted American trial lawyer and advisor to some of the most powerful people in the worlds of politics, business, and entertainment, Louis Nizer, once wrote:

"Words of comfort, skilfully administered, are the oldest therapy known to man."

There is perhaps no other place better to witness the effect of such skilful words of comfort than at a hospice.

At Keech, the importance of providing a soothing word alongside a listening ear has led to the development of many of its family support services – from bereavement care to peer-group sessions.

Soon after the adult hospice opened, a peer support group was set up called 'Silver Lining'.

Run by members of the original nursing team, the group enabled people who were recently bereaved to meet with others in a similar situation and talk about their feelings and loss.

It was such a successful initiative that the groups are still run to this very day, as are the hospice's well-known remembrance events, 'Daffodil Sunday' and the 'Service of Remembrance' held at St. Margaret's Church in Streatley.

After a few years, however, the hospice team realised there was a gap in service in terms of one-to-one support, something which might particularly be needed for those who were unable to travel to the hospice and would be better supported at home. Matron in 1996, Barbara Kettley, called upon Jeff Lewcock to help set up such a service.

Jeff had been working as a counsellor, setting up the 'Talking Therapies' service with Luton Primary Healthcare Trust, but volunteered with the hospice on his day off.

Recalling the thinking behind the Bereavement Visitor Service, Jeff, who is now a full-time Bereavement Care Manager at the hospice, said:

"Death, dying and grief are all natural occurrences, part of life. Research showed us that in many cases, people have their own support system at home or within their community. But there are some who don't have this and our idea was to replicate it. We didn't want to use staff or anyone with a 'care' label already attached to them but instead brought in 'normal' every day people as volunteers and trained them up, giving them the skills they needed to

listen. This way, our service became quite natural – it was simply the community supporting itself."

Promoting the opportunity of becoming a Bereavement Visitor in local newspapers, the hospice advert stated:

> We are looking for people with sensitivity, warmth, commitment and strength. Above all, we are looking for people who can listen with total attention, who can withhold from giving their own personal interpretations or advice and can sustain silence as an acknowledgement that words are sometimes inadequate.

Out of 21 applicants, 19 people were interviewed and 16 were selected to initially attend a bereavement care course. After this, those who were still interested, were interviewed again and 13 became the first set of volunteers. These were: Eileen Bird, Finbarr Callan, Harry Dobkin, Ann Evans, Diana Freeman, Elizabeth Gillespie, Sheila Girling, Pauline Capell, Edna Lawrence, Roy Pinnock, Kathleen Scott, Denise Tysoe and Brenda Whitcroft. On completion of that first course, back in 1996, Edna Lawrence wrote to the hospice, saying:

"Like many people, because I've experienced grief and bereavement myself, I thought I understood it. Wrong!! [The course was] interesting, eye-opening and educational. It made me realise just what a complex subject it is, but above all, it made me understand how much I would like to be involved as a Bereavement Visitor."

Edna and fellow volunteer, Brenda Whitcroft, are the only members of the original group who continue to volunteer with the service some 15 years later. Still fully supervised and supported at the hospice by Jeff, neither they nor any of the other Bereavement Visitors are professional counsellors.

T hey do not give advice but are skilled and trained at listening, comforting and helping people to work out their own emotions and feelings. Jeff commented:

"It often takes a while for these volunteers to realise the impact of what they do. Many see it as just giving up an hour of their time once a week – no big deal. But it is clearly much more than that and the feedback we've had proves it – time and again people comment on the same things – how useful it was to have someone to talk to, to have no judgements made and not to feel silly."

Jeff Lewcock and Judith Groom

Here's what just some users of the service had to say:

"The Bereavement Visitor service is a wonderful thing and has helped me to cope with the loss of my husband. Just being able to talk to my visitor was a great comfort and support when I needed it most during a very difficult time."

"The service has given me the strength to carry on with my life. I'm so used to having to look after someone else, I am able to put me first, I can be a bit selfish and not feel guilty about it. My chats have given me so much more, being able to laugh and cry."

"It helped to have someone to talk to who was outside the family because I could say what I was feeling inside, things too upsetting for my family to hear. To an 'outsider', I could say what was in my heart."

Jane and Emma

At a time when the Silver Lining group and Bereavement Visitor Service had been helping people at the adult hospice overcome the loss of a loved one for 15 years and 10 years respectively, the charity began to look more closely at how it could help families grieving the death of a child.

Support for such families had always been available, offered quite intuitively as part of the care team's role, but in 2006, Keech launched a new support group for parents, grandparents and other adult family members. With guidance from staff at the hospice, the aim was for them to help each other come to terms with the loss of a child in the family. Aptly, the first group to meet named themselves, 'Shoulders of Support' or SOS. Bereavement Care Worker at that time, Judith Groom explained:

"We talk about the children and how the family feels after their death. The support group is really intended to show the family that they aren't alone. We hope they can build friendships with others in a similar situation and overcome their loss together."

Andy and Jane attended one of the earliest SOS groups alongside Jane's parents. All were grieving the loss of Jane and Andy's daughter, Emma, who had died the previous year, aged three. Andy perhaps summed up the importance of SOS best when he said:

"It's probably the worst thing to have in common with another person, but it's so special to reflect on the time you had with your child. You have the utmost respect for other people and their stories. Each of you has lost a child, but you've also gained something in coming to SOS."

Paul and Carolyn Wright joined the SOS group in 2007. The couple's daughter, Zoë had a cancerous brain tumour which proved very aggressive and led to her death just months after her diagnosis.

At the time, Carolyn said:

"After going to the first session, Paul wasn't sure whether this was right for him, however he is still attending. Everyone deals with these things differently and I felt very comfortable about going.

"What I've found most helpful is seeing people who are that bit further down the line and seeing they are still in one piece and look OK. That makes you think you can get through it too."

Because of its ethos of enveloping the whole family and not just the sick child, the children's hospice knew from day one that there was a need to support the brothers and sisters of children in its care. Based on what other children's hospices and also CHUMS, a child bereavement charity, were doing, the care team at Keech were involved in supporting siblings both pre and post bereavement.

From 2005, as the numbers of siblings needing this kind of support increased, the hospice identified the need for a dedicated Sibling Support Worker who could provide one-to-one support and help these children to alleviate some of their emotional stress and worries through a combination of activities and discussions. Taking on that role, Jo Goode explained:

"The support is based around the understanding we have of how having a sibling with special needs can impact on a child's day-to-day life and also the added effect of the condition being life-limiting. The support is provided through one-to-one sessions or working with siblings from the same family together. This may be a short piece of work done over a number of set sessions (to be extended as necessary) or ongoing support, depending on what is needed.

"The children often like playing games and doing creative activities, but sometimes they just want to share their worries with someone other than a parent. Working on a one-to-one basis gives the children some special attention and provides the opportunity for them to make a new, supportive friend."

In June 2005, Keech began running a bi-monthly support group for 5-12 year old siblings – the Keech Sparklers Club.

Held on a Saturday morning and supported by a small team of dedicated volunteers, the objective was to help children deal with the emotional effect of having a brother or sister with complex care needs, allow them to meet other children their own age with similar experiences, and to have some fun.

The groups were also seen as a good opportunity for staff and volunteers to build relationships with children that may need further support in the future.

Still running today, the group offers the children a range of activities – from nature walks to dance and movement sessions, from making family trees to learning circus skills. Around the time when the group was being set up, Human Resources Manager at GlaxoSmithKline, Katrina Hoskins applied to become a volunteer at Keech.

Keen to work directly with families in some way, as opposed to providing administrative or fundraising support, Katrina became one of the first to help Jo Goode run the club. She added:

"We focused the sessions on children as healthy siblings who inevitably feel left out when attentions turn to the sick child. Through peer support, creativity, imagination and play the group shared their similar experiences and felt less isolated as a result.

"As the workshops could be emotionally challenging, we also held a few fun days throughout the year purely for the children to enjoy themselves, doing activities that they cannot usually access with their families due to the needs of their brother or sister, with the aim of also giving parents a break for the day!"

Continuing their story, Carolyn Wright spoke of how Zoë's brother, Thomas, benefitted from sibling support. After being visited at home a few times, Thomas became a member of the Sparklers Club. Carolyn said:

"Thomas was obviously put at ease at the Sparkler's Club because, by the second session, he was able to stand up and talk about Zoë. He came out so happy and couldn't wait to go back again. As parents, Paul and I are trying to get through this ourselves and support Thomas too. It's hard to know if you're doing things right so it's been great that Thomas gets this extra support from Keech."

The Wright family

Following the same principle as the Sparklers Club but adapting it for 13-19 year olds, Keech launched its second support group, Teendays in 2007. The aim was identical – to give these children and young people the opportunity to work out their own feelings about their brother or sister's illness, meet with those in a similar situation to themselves and provide them with some enjoyable (and in some cases unique) experiences.

In January 2008, six members of the group took part in a scuba diving session in the hospice's own hydrotherapy pool, carried out free of charge by three professional scuba diving instructors. Jo Goode said:

"Many of the young people who attend Teendays get to enjoy special and unique experiences – often things that their friends outside of Teendays are unlikely to get the chance to do. However, they deserve it as they miss out on so much at other times. The scuba diving session was a great experience for them. Many were quite nervous but they soon got to grips with it and ended up really enjoying it."

Following from the success of its peer groups for adult relatives and siblings of the children at the hospice, Keech began to look at how this type of support might work for the life-limited children themselves. As a result, two new groups were introduced in 2007 – 'Peer-to Peer' for a group of boys aged 11 – 16 who had been diagnosed with Muscular Dystrophy and 'Girls Aloud' for teenage girls with a range of life-limiting conditions. Whilst the aim of both groups was to provide a place for these young people to talk openly, meet others socially, support each other and gain a taste of independence away from their parents, in some ways the groups have also become part of the hospice's provision of bereavement support. Bereavement Care Manager, Jeff Lewcock explained:

"These are children who are still alive, but bereavement can begin long before a death. Bereavement and loss starts with the diagnosis – it's something which is felt by the family and the patient themselves. We felt that the more support we can give to people pre-bereavement, the more it helps to ease their journey."

Initially, six boys joined the 'Peer-to-Peer' group and met on six separate Saturdays at Keech between May – July 2007. With the support of staff, each session generally included a combination of some therapeutic time such as group discussions and the opportunity to talk to the hospice doctor, followed by fun time such as using the play station, playing wheelchair football or making pizza. Integral to its set-up, the children's hospice Social Worker of this time, Sharon Kelly said:

Peer-to-Peer group getting ready for an activity holiday

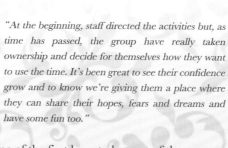

"At the beginning, staff directed the activities but, as time has passed, the group have really taken ownership and decide for themselves how they want to use the time. It's been great to see their confidence grow and to know we're giving them a place where they can share their hopes, fears and dreams and have some fun too."

One of the first boys to be part of the group was fifteen year old Aaron. He said:

"I really enjoy coming to Peer-to-Peer, I get to speak to people with the same condition as me and being here just makes you feel like a normal person for the day. We can play on the Playstation, go swimming or visit the music room but the best thing about the day is just socialising and talking to others."

Even before the set-up of 'Peer-to-Peer', Keech recognised the therapeutic benefits of giving the children and young people opportunities to enjoy social situations their healthy peers could do.

Back in 2004, Nursing Manager, Jo McDonnell, Pool Manager, Jim Casey, and Care Assistant, Steve Andrews, took two boys with Muscular Dystrophy to watch Manchester United play Everton. Now a Bereavement Care Worker, Steve remembers:

"It's one of my most precious memories. The two lads we took, Peter and John, were both huge Man United fans. It was a cold day to say the least and it ended 0 – 0. But the crowning moment for me came about 15 minutes into the second half. There was lots of shouting and cheering as you would expect, but suddenly I was hearing language only sailors would use coming from my right. Being one of the 'adults' with these young people I turned to see who was berating the players in this way. To my surprise (and amusement) it was John! The air was blue but I was so proud to be able to give that young man the opportunity to be like anyone else for just one day!"

Siblings enjoy some outdoor activities

When words are not enough

For a place like Keech Hospice Care, the value of talking, listening and sharing experiences is obvious, but there are, of course, times when words are not enough. The development of the more physical and sensory therapies at Keech has proved just as important to the overall benefit of patients and their families from both hospices.

For some the idea of a massage or reflexology session may seem a luxury but not so at Keech. With a determination to provide a holistic service to its patients and families right from the very start, ways other than medical and nursing interventions had to be found to take account of the spiritual and mental (as well as physical) well-being of people coming to Keech. Complementary therapies were becoming more widely known and soon a team of volunteer therapists began providing various therapies – mainly to Day Hospice patients. Here's how just some of those therapies work:

Indian Head Massage: This therapy began over 400 years ago and is useful for relaxation, stress relief, scalp conditions and sinus problems.

Reflexology: This is based on the idea that every area on the foot represents a different area of the body. By massaging the relevant area of the foot you can help bring the corresponding part of the body back into balance.

Aromatherapy: This involves using essential oils to help with different ailments (e.g. lavender is soothing, while ginger can help with circulation). The oils can be added to baths, used in massage or in aroma-streams.

In 2003, the contribution of complementary therapies to palliative care was finally officially recognised with the publication of National Guidelines for the Use of Complementary Therapies in Supportive and Palliative Care. This also meant that the charity had to change the way it managed and provided these therapies to ensure they met with the newly published guidelines. To do this, the charity employed its first paid Complementary Therapy Coordinator. Time and time again since then, these treatments have been shown to significantly help relieve stress and anxiety, invoke a relaxed state of mind and offer relief from physical pain. From October 2006 onwards, the coordinator and a team of volunteer therapists, began visiting families out in the community.

Complementary therapies at Keech and the hydrotherapy pool (through the window)

Taking on the role of Complementary Therapy Coordinator at the hospice today, Roger Kelly, commented on the benefits he sees patients and their family members experience through such therapies:

"Either having a life-limiting condition or supporting someone with an illness can be stressful. Complementary therapies can offer an oasis of calm in what is often a discomforting experience. Therapies are offered in a variety of areas: either during regular visits to day care services, during in-patient stays or as part of an out-patient programme. For some, access to complementary therapies serves as an introduction to the hospice and the support we provide.

"Over the last few years, we have been able to offer an increased number of therapy sessions, with patients and carers now being seen every weekday. We also work in conjunction with the Music Therapy department to offer relaxation sessions as well as Music and Massage – a unique blend of live music and gentle massage – which has proven beneficial in helping some of our more anxious patients to find some calm."

Since it opened in 2002, the hydrotherapy pool at Keech has provided further means of therapeutic support for patients and their families. Heated to a temperature of 34 degrees, the pool is a lot warmer than a normal swimming pool which means patients with a very wide range of conditions can swim in comfort.

For some, the pool is an extension of their physiotherapy treatment or a means of stimulating stiff or aching muscles; for others it's a chance to experience a multi-sensory environment with the flashing pool side lights, fountains and under water music. Some use it simply for the chance to relax, but for a significant number of patients whose conditions prohibit them from going to a public pool, the hydrotherapy pool is the only opportunity for them to enjoy a swim. Hydrotherapy Pool Coordinator, Jim Casey explains further:

"The pool has a lot of therapeutic benefits as well as helping people with treatment. You see people using the pool for the first time and their worries are momentarily lifted as they ease into the heated water and start to unwind. It really is a joy to watch and I often find people's attitudes very inspiring."

Louise Brazier's son, James, was diagnosed with Restrictive Cardiomyopathy at 4 months old and received care at Keech before he died in 2011. Louise remembers the effect that the hydrotherapy pool had on her family:

"The most memorable time for us at Keech has to be the first time we took James swimming in the hydrotherapy pool. Because of his poorly heart, James's hands and feet are often very cold and his body becomes mottled. We've never been able to take him to a public pool but the hydrotherapy pool at Keech is much warmer. We were still a little nervous about taking him into the water but it was amazing. James absolutely loved it. We had never seen him move his arms and legs so much and I think if I had let go he may actually have started swimming! He was smiling and laughing and splashing.

"Seeing our little boy so happy was a very special experience. For this hour all the worries had gone and we just had pure fun!"

Providing another means of support, music, and music therapy, has been a part of life at Keech since the service was established in 2000. With his previous experience of the benefits of Music Therapy from his time at the Cambridge Children's Hospices, Mike Keel was determined this should be provided at the new Keech Cottage Children's Hospice. He went one step further and included the adult hospice too.

"Mike approached two charities...."

Mike approached two charities that supported music therapy in palliative care, The Towersey Foundation and Jessie's Fund, who provided funding to adult and children's hospices respectively. The two charities had not worked together before and their approaches were slightly different in how they gave their support, but, with gentle negotiation and a promise of a truly innovative service across a children's and adult hospice, they agreed to fund a music therapist for four days a week at the charity. From this original part-time post, the hospice now employs two music therapists who support patients and their families in the hospice and in the community.

Graeme's Romanian trip

The original post holder, Graeme Davis, became so specialised and proficient in his role that, in 2003, he was invited to spend a week at the Hospice Casa Sperantei in Brasov, Romania to share his experience and to forge links with this organisation. This was a life-changing experience for Graeme and the staff were enthralled on his return when he gave a presentation and displayed his photographs.

Writing of his experiences at the time, Graeme said:

"During my time at Casa Sperantei I had many enjoyable experiences, but two in particular come to mind. On my first day, when I entered the children's daycare area, one of the children was making some sounds on a glockenspiel. I went immediately to the keyboard and began to reflect and imitate the quality and pitches of his sounds. He immediately responded, aware of the connection that was being made. Mara, the play therapist, encouraged the other children to join in, offering instruments and facilitating those who needed extra help. Before long we had a vibrant music group going. The language barrier prevented me from understanding what the children said and vice versa. However it did not matter. We had created musical ideas that we were able to share and experience spontaneously together.

"The other episode was similar - when I was invited to demonstrate some active music making ideas to the adult patients. Following an initial demonstration by the lead daycare nurse and myself, one of the patients began improvising on a drum. I improvised music on the keyboard to support her sounds. Then, in order to develop the music, I began to sing a melody. The lady immediately joined in singing. Before long we were exploring all kinds of strange and wonderful voice sounds. The other patients joined in, either by singing or clapping along or simply by smiling and laughing. The whole atmosphere of the group had changed to one of vibrant life and of sharing experiences.

A fly on the wall in the music room at Keech would witness everything from pure laugh-out-loud occasions to heart-wrenching moments.

"Before I left for Brasov I had no idea what to expect. What I experienced at Casa Sperantei was an openness towards learning new skills and great integrity towards the care of the patients. For my part, it gave me an opportunity to experience hospice life from a different perspective. This is so important in maintaining and developing one's understanding of working in a hospice and the overall hospice philosophy. "

Describing the different approaches to the use of music in therapy, the British Association for Music therapy states:

"Depending on the needs of the client and the orientation of the therapist, different aspects of the work may be emphasised. Fundamental to all approaches, however, is the development of a relationship between the client and therapist. Music-making forms the basis for communication in this relationship."

Following this principle, music therapy at Keech involves creating a relationship with a patient/client through the medium of music. The hospice music therapists do not teach their clients to play an instrument or to sing, but rather encourage them to play, sing or simply listen to music in ways that help them work with their feelings and emotions and express them in a way that they may be unable to do in words. As well as this, music therapy has been shown to help people deal with anxiety, depression, insomnia, isolation, relaxation, loss and bereavement. Through a combination of group and individual sessions, music therapy at Keech has helped a countless number of patients and family members in all of these ways. Because these people all have such different needs, a fly on the wall in the music room at Keech would witness everything from pure laugh-out-loud occasions to heart-wrenching moments.

One example of how the atmosphere can change quite rapidly in music therapy can be seen in the Tuesday Listening Group. Established in 2007, this group of adult patients, who decided early on that they didn't want to play any instruments, come together each week to listen to music of their choice. Music Therapist at the hospice today, Anna Ludwig said:

"It's an open group and patients are invited to bring along music of their choice to listen to with other members of the group. This can often lead to a very eclectic hour of music, and can be quite an education! Sometimes the talk is fairly general; chatting about the weather, the music itself or nothing at all. At other times, patients use the time to talk about their hopes and fears, their beliefs and wishes."

A second example of just how poignant music therapy can be comes from a young girl, Alice's story. Here it is:

Alice's Story...

"I hope you enjoy the music that I'm playing and that it helps you fall asleep."

The nurses in the adult In-patient Unit were concerned about 8 year-old Alice who found it very hard being in the room with her dad who was at the hospice and nearing the end stages of his life. Alice was unable to stay in the room and couldn't find anything to say to her dad, a situation which put everyone on edge – staff, family and dad. Alice was referred for music therapy sessions to help her address her fears and (as it turned out) her anger. At the time, no one was quite sure how much Alice understood about her dad's condition so, after spending some time with the music therapist, Alice's mum asked her to try to find out more.

Alice loved the opportunity to get out of the In-patient Unit and to do something creative, something she could do herself without anyone else telling how to. She could be as noisy as she liked and let off lots and lots of steam using the drum kit and some wonderful instruments called "Boom whackers"! She was in control and in a safe environment.

After a couple of sessions, the music therapist talked with Alice about her dad. Alice clearly did not want to discuss this but did think it would be nice to record some music for her dad in the hope that it makes him happy and helps him to sleep. Using various instruments and recording equipment, Alice made a multi-layered track for her dad, on which she proudly tells him about the instruments she uses while the music plays:

Nice daddy, this music is for you.
I made the music for you and I played all the instruments.

First I played the harp, then the metallophone.
Then the rain-stick, then the wind-chimes.

I hope my music makes you happy and relaxed, because it's calm music.
From little me.
I hope you enjoy the music that I'm playing and that it helps you fall asleep."

This gave Alice a voice that could be left in her dad's room when she found it too hard to be with him. She knew that he could hear her voice and know that she cares.

In the summer of 2007, the music therapy team launched a new 'Music on Wheels' service, designed to take music therapy out of the hospice and into patients' homes. Made possible by a number of generous grants and donations (including from the Lehman Brothers Foundation Europe, Jessie's Fund, The Towersey Foundation, The Joron Charitable Trust and 'Souls and Shadows'), this was an exciting new development. At the time, Graeme Davis commented:

Music therapist, Kathryn Barker with Glenn Harrison

"Previously patients could only access music therapy when they came into the hospice. If they had hospital appointments or issues with transport it would mean we wouldn't see them. The new project means that we can now access more people in need of emotional support as well as providing greater continuity of treatment for existing patients."

In 2009, teenage patient, Cameron's mum, Karen described the impact this had on her family:

"Kathryn, the music therapist comes out to us once a week and it's something that we all get involved in. For me, music therapy is a rare opportunity to see Cameron and his younger brother, Glenn, do something together. There's not much they can do on the same level but music therapy gives them a real chance to have fun and it brings them closer together. Most importantly, it lets Cameron take a bit of control. In his every day life, we make all the decisions for him – when he eats, where he goes, when he goes to bed. In music therapy we've been shown techniques that help him to play but allow him to direct things for himself. He selects his instruments and chooses how he plays – fast, slow, loud, quiet, when he starts and when he wants to stop. It's one of the few times he can make definite decisions for himself – and it's lovely to see him have that taste of freedom."

June 2011 saw some new developments from within the music therapy service – the first ever joint adult and children's service music therapy group and the hospice's participation in the first 'National Music Therapy Week'. Commenting on both, Anna Ludwig said:

"Bringing together our patients was daunting but turned into one of the most fantastic experiences ever as adult patients joined in with our silly songs and played with the children. Then, to celebrate national Music Therapy week, we engaged volunteers to play live music in the hospice for seven hours on the trot and formed the very first "Hospice Kazoo Orchestra" – what a lively, musical experience that was!"

Anna Ludwig with Keech families during Music Therapy Week 2011

and Finally...

Day care at the children's hospice

Over the last 21 years, what is now Keech Hospice Care has seen so many changes and development in its care, there just isn't enough space in this book to list them all. There's been the development of a blood transfusion and lymphoedema service at the adult hospice; the introduction of a 24-hour advice line; the launch of partnership project with the charity 'Sense' in 2009 to provide day care for young people aged 16-25 with sensory impairment and severe disabilities; and the development of a younger children's day care service in 2011 which supports children and young people through specialist play and educational activities while also offering short day time breaks for their parents and carers.

While all of this has taken place, no-one should forget the contribution made by support staff, the unsung heroes at the hospice such as the finance team that have helped the hospice cope through thick and thin. Then there are the housekeeping and maintenance teams. From a handful of volunteers in the early days, Keech now has three members of staff in its maintenance team and nine in its housekeeping team. Alongside several volunteers, these are the people who, behind the scenes, keep the expanded buildings at the hospices fit for their purpose, safe and hygienic. If the lights weren't fixed, the beds unchanged, the floors not swept or the walls left unpainted, none of what Keech has actually achieved over the years could have taken place.

However, when it comes to the charity's achievements, the final word must go to a family support event that has been run by the hospice since 1994. Starting life as 'Lights of Love' and taking on the national branding of 'Light up a Life' in 2009, this event has literally brought thousands of people to the hospice – each one remembering and celebrating the life of loved one, whether they had been a patient at the hospice or not.

At the first event in 1994, the tree was officially lit by Mrs Joan Bartholomew, the widow of comedian, Eric Morecombe and around 250 members of the public, staff and volunteers turned up for the ceremony. Each light on the tree represented a dedication made by someone to their loved one, placed in return for a donation of £5 or more. Over the years, the event has essentially remained the same, including readings from volunteers and staff members, personal accounts from relatives of patients that have been cared for at the hospice, hymns and other special songs and the switching on of the lights on the hospice's Christmas tree. Even the dedications are still made for the same level of donation – just £5.

However, this is an event which has never been run as a 'fundraiser' for the hospice. Even as the numbers of people attending has reached almost 1000 each year, the event retains its central purpose which is rooted in care.The event goes much further than being a simple gathering of people. It involves a shared moment where people's memories are brought to the forefront; it is a clear demonstration of the comfort people give to each other; it invokes many tears but is a manifest of the way the hospice has cared for local people over the last two decades.

Having volunteered at the service for many years, Shirley Noller talked of her experience:

"I have always enjoyed the service. I loved meeting relatives of patients who I had become close to by working on the unit. Although it was a sad occasion, it was a privilege to share it with them."

In 2008, Sarah Bates was one of the relatives who gave a speech at the service. Summing up what Light up a Life means to so many, she said:

"When I first came to the service, it was the year my husband, Rob, had died in the care of the wonderful staff at the hospice. The event was charged with emotion but to me it was the most natural way to remember Rob and the life we had shared. A year later, I was asked to speak at the service. That was even more emotional but what an honour and a privilege to be part of this event. I did it for Rob, and all our family, and was overwhelmed by the love we were surrounded by. To me, the lights on that tree depicted the linked hands – the embrace – of light and love that I feel at the hospice. At events like this we may all be strangers on the surface but we are not alone, and neither is Rob, on his new journey."

Sarah Bates and other special guests with staff at Lights of Love 2008

Scenes from the First Lights of Love in 1994

"To me, the lights on that tree depicted the linked hands - the embrace - of light and love I feel at the hospice. At events like this we may all be strangers on the surface but we are not alone, and neither is Rob, on his new journey."

Catherine's
STORY

"A phone call became our life-line."

My mum, Catherine, was diagnosed with lung cancer in February 2010 and in the year that followed her condition fluctuated and she had various admissions to hospital. After being discharged from one of those hospital visits in March 2011, we were given the number of the Palliative Care Advice Line, operated by Keech Hospice Care. It became our life-line.

We had not long returned from the hospital when Mum became very poorly again. Her syringe driver had not been set up and she was in quite a lot of pain. She also felt like she couldn't breathe and was panicking so I called the advice line.

I spoke to a nurse who calmed me down and assured me I was doing the right things to help Mum while waiting for a district nurse to arrive. It had been a horrendous situation at home, but the caring, kind and reassuring voice on the end of the line was a huge help.

The next day, Keech had arranged to visit Mum at home to assess her condition and recommended that she went into the hospice for some pain management. When we got there it was like a weight lifted off our shoulders. Everyone was very approachable and the atmosphere was fantastic.

Mum was settled into a wonderful room, a doctor came to see us almost immediately and we were all so well looked after. After a week at the hospice, Mum returned home for a while but, towards the end of April, she took a turn for the worse. I was unable to get her to take her medications and so called the advice line at Keech again. Once more they were fantastic. The next day someone came out to see us and confirmed my fears that things were nearing an end. Dad went to the hospice with Mum that night and she passed away the following day. Although that still brings us incredible sadness, the memory of Mum's last hours at Keech is a good one. She was in a beautiful room with the breeze coming in through the patio doors and looked serene and relaxed. The whole experience at Keech was amazing, from the reassurance I got over the advice line to the wonderful care offered to Mum, to the way we were given space to grieve. To have this place where we could turn to for help has truly been invaluable.

Jane, Catherine's daughter

Catherine Tierney

"To have this place where we could turn to for help has truly been invaluable."

Matthew's
STORY

When Matthew was born, he seemed to be very quiet and content. We thought ourselves lucky to have such a chilled out baby. But, from the time he was around three months old, we knew that something wasn't right. He hadn't yet smiled, was floppy and then he started to have hic-up like jumps. At first, the doctors thought these might be due to poor eyesight, but we knew it was more than that. Three days before his first Christmas, we were given the news that Matthew had a condition called Myoclonic epilepsy.

From then onwards we were thrown into a completely alien world of medicine. Over his first year, Matthew had endless tests and procedures – CT scans, MRIs, ECGs and blood tests, but most of these kept coming back negative. Slowly, the added complications unfolded and, as well as his rare type of epilepsy, he had global developmental delay, asthma, various allergies and suffered from reflux and choking. During his short life, he was unable to walk or talk, had lots of chest issues and was eventually fed through a gastro tube. He had various surgical procedures and needed an ever-changing cocktail of medication and feeds.

In spite of all of this, Matthew was cheeky and mischievous and didn't let his condition stop him. He worked hard to learn his own ways of doing things like rolling to where he wanted to be or letting us know how he was feeling with just a raise of an eyebrow! He was generally happy and only cried when something was seriously wrong.

When Matthew was two years old, we were referred to Keech and initially had a community nurse who helped us with Matthew's care at home. This was like having a good friend who could be your sounding block but also had so much knowledge and understanding. We went on to use many of the services offered by Keech – overnight stays, hydrotherapy, music therapy, Tots & Toys sessions, complementary therapy and now, bereavement care. Keech provided a complete package for our family. People often think a hospice is about dying, but what Keech did for us was to help us focus on the day-to-day – living a fulfilling life while preparing for what the future holds.

Keech showed us we didn't have to do it alone. As the parent of a child with such complex health needs you put walls up to protect yourself. At Keech you can lose the 'tough mummy' front and have a crisis moment if you need it, tissues and all. There are no consequences to your actions – you can just be whoever you need to be. But although there's tears, the hospice is not a sad place. It's OK to laugh and giggle and there's a lot of that going too! In August 2009, our lives changed forever. Matthew's health had been good and we'd had a phenomenal summer – going out and about everywhere we could – to the zoo, on picnics, theme parks – everything a family would normally do with their kids in the summer holidays.

But then, Matthew had a very high temperature and started to be very sick. He was taken to hospital and over the next few days had to fight a bad chest infection while suffering from of a new type of massive seizure. Medically this proved impossible and eventually, we had to take the heart breaking decision to change his care to palliative. He was still on medication to control his pain and seizures but all the other tubes came out and as soon as we could, we moved Matthew to Keech.

"At Keech you can lose the 'tough tummy' front and have a crisis moment if you need it, tissues and all."

When we arrived, we physically felt our shoulders go down. We were surrounded by people who knew us all and, for the last few days of his life, Matthew had no more pain or seizures. The music therapy ladies played the harp to him and there was always someone for us to talk to – people who had been with us all the way throughout our journey. It had been our wish to take Matthew for end of life care at Keech and when Matthew died so peacefully there, we knew it was the right place for us to be.

Ever since that time, Keech is still a big part of our family. We've had bereavement counselling and I've especially been grateful for the support I've had from Kathryn, one of the hospice's music therapists.

It's not really music therapy as you might think of it. At times Kathryn and I will just sit and talk. Sometimes all you need is to say something out loud. We've worked on some poems and putting them to music – we've almost got an album! I think I'm on the last one now though – a grand finale really. It's helping me accept our journey – life before we had Keech, life with Keech there to support us, saying goodbye, and reaching a place where life can move forward again.

Carolyn Heard, Matthew's Mum

"People often think a hospice is about dying, but what Keech did for us was to help us focus on the day-to-day - living a fulfilling life while preparing for what the future holds."

((Top) Matthew's family, Matthew's stepping stone and Carolyn and Matthew

MATTHEW HEARD
Fulfilled Life
and
Precious Times

Chapter Sixteen

Fundraising for Keech

Fundraising for Keech,
Where do we begin.
There's so much to say,
So much to fit in.
So here's a wee taste,
Let's call it a speech,
On what people have done,
To care for Keech.

And there were...

Barn dances and lottery chances,
Dressing up and footie cups,
Shaving heads and Santa's sleds,
Skydiving and rally driving,
Polar treks and giant cheques,
Waxing chests and marathon quests,
Market stalls and black-tie balls,
Quiz nights and Christmas lights,
Tea at three and wine with brie,
Midnight walks and church hall talks,
Summer shows and boxing blows,
Custard baths and lots of laughs,
...PHEW!

Hilary Corfan

With such a wide variety of fundraising efforts, it seems there's little people won't do for Keech! From those who sold tea towels to raise money for the original adult hospice building to those who take on the challenge of an overseas trek today and everything in between, the results have been truly amazing.

From an initial target of £1.5 million to open the original adult hospice, in its 21st year Keech Hospice Care needed the slightly staggering sum of £7.8 million to run the entire charity operation. Of this, £1.3m came from statutory funding and another £3.2m came from the retail operation and other sources. That left the charity's fundraising team with a target of £3.3m to raise in voluntary income, for instance from individual donations, events, clubs, lottery players, legacies and local businesses. And so, while the activities involved in fundraising are sometimes a little crazy, funny and eccentric, the business of raising money for Keech is a serious matter. As time has passed, the fundraising team at Keech has necessarily grown in number to coordinate and manage all of these different means of raising income.

A recently reired member of the Fundraising team, Hilary Corfan, spoke of her time with the charity:

"I joined the Fundraising team in 2003. After helping out as a volunteer for a few years I was delighted to be given the opportunity to become a professional fundraiser for such a wonderful local cause. Over the years I have been privileged to work with many staff and volunteers whose dedication to raising much-needed income has been extraordinary. There are lots of qualities which are fundamental to a good fundraiser; organisational skills, energy, confidence and a sense of humour spring to mind but the most important ingredient is PASSION. I can honestly say that I have met hundreds of passionate fundraisers during my 12 happy years at Keech Hospice Care."

Over the years, fundraising at Keech has always involved a wide range of areas – the flagship events, the unusual or quirky moments and what it has come to see as its 'bread and butter', for instance the Smiley Sam adventure that takes place every year and the relentless efforts of those who stand for hours with collection boxes on the charity's behalf.

Regardless of the size or scale of the effort, every act of fundraising for Keech has made its contribution – in effect become one of the building blocks that help the charity achieve those challenging financial targets year after year.Take Smiley Sam for example. It brings around £40,000 a year, but what lies behind the figures is perhaps more poignant. For fifteen years, as the Christmas float has been making its rounds around local streets, hundreds of volunteers have got involved and literally thousands of local children and their families have enjoyed and grown up with the sight of Santa at their doorsteps.

Similarly, there are a number of other fundraising events and campaigns which have proved memorable in the minds of the public, quite a number of which seem to have involved walking or running challenges.

" There are lots of qualities which are fundamental to a good fundraiser; organisational skills, energy, confidence and a sense of humour spring to mind but the most important ingredient is

Passion... "

Putting the best foot forward

In 1999, the hospice sent its first team along to the Flora Light Women's Challenge, a 5km fun run held in Hyde Park. Made up of just ten ladies, many of whom were staff, they managed to raise a sum of around £1,000. Over the next few years the popularity of the event grew rapidly and by 2002 the hospice sent a team of 262 women who raised £26,600.

Heading down to Hyde Park in double-decker buses, provided free of charge by Arriva with drivers who volunteered their time too, those who took part remember it as a real outing. One of the first to take part, Nicola Field, said:

"Even at the beginning, when we were just a small team, we still had lots of fun and then as more and more people took part the atmosphere going down on the buses was brilliant. Everybody enjoyed the challenge and felt a real connection with each other, knowing we were all there to raise money for the hospice."

More locally, another event which took off from the beginning was the Walk on the Wildside. Initiated by the Fundraising Committee lead by Jack Sapsworth, the 3-mile walk took place at Luton Hoo from the early 1990's until the estate began its transformation into a hotel in 2003. The following year, it moved to Stockwood Park and then around 2005, it moved again to Woburn Abbey. Popular with families, many brought buggies and dogs along, some took part in fancy dress and some even did the walk on stilts.

Some of the ladies who took part in the hospice's Women's Challenge for Keech

Lorna Solomon and Shauna McLean made a special effort in 2006, raising over £150 when they did the walk dressed as fairies. They were joined by Lorna's mum, Anne, who said:

"Dressing up for the walk was a good way to involve teenagers in fundraising activities, and the three mile walk was good exercise for all of us!"

Unfortunately, by 2007, the numbers of participants and the money raised for the hospice through the Women's Challenge and Walk on the Wildside had begun to decline. In effect, both events had run their course, but the accolades they achieved during their time should not be forgotten. At its peak, the hospice team for the women's challenge created a massive presence at a national event. In total, the challenge involved around 400 ladies, many of whom took part several years in a row and brought in a total of £93,480 for the charity. Similarly, a total of 710 different walkers joined the Walk on the Wildside over the years, raising a sum of £92,202.

In need of a fresh idea which would attract the large numbers again, Keech launched its first Midnight Walk in Luton in 2008.

As a 10 mile sponsored walk for ladies only, starting at the stroke of Midnight, the event was promoted as the 'Saturday night out with a difference'.

Scenes from Walk on the Wild Side between 2002-2005
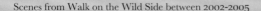

The charity was overwhelmed by the response as 1001 local ladies signed up to walk on the night of Saturday 6th September. It was even more delighted to see that the event had proved to be its most successful to date, raising a staggering £133,000.

Popular with ladies of all ages, one particular story of courage that year came from 87 year-old Dorothy Dimmock from Luton.

Dorothy, the oldest walker on the night, completed the walk in under 3½ hours and said:

> "People have been telling me I'm mad to be taking part but they have still sponsored me and wished me luck! I have been praying that I'd get round the 10 miles but I took a wheelchair for when things got a bit tricky and I had my good friend Louise to push me some of the way. I was just keeping my fingers crossed that I'd finish the walk in time for my granddaughter's 40th Birthday the following day!"

Recognising and building on its success, the following year, Keech decided to hold a series of walks – one in Stevenage, one in Bedford and another in Luton. Collectively they raised £163,000.

Still bringing in substantial funds today, nearly 4,500 women have joined the Midnight Walks to date. Between them, the ladies have covered enough miles to go twice around the world!

Many of the participants have entered alongside family, friends or work colleagues, dressed up for the occasion and enjoyed the buzz of the night.

However, some have had particularly strong reasons for taking part. Jo Snell joined the Stevenage walk in 2009 along with twelve friends. At that time, Jo's 4 year-old daughter, who had Tetraplegic Cerebral Palsy, came under the care of the children's hospice. After completing the walk, Jo said:

> "I have been amazed by the support from my friends for this event. They know how much Keech has helped Rosie and me and realise that it would be hard to cope with the everyday struggles that a terminally ill child brings without the support of this fantastic place."

Alongside the development of its night-time walks, in recent years, Keech has expanded its offering of sponsored events to include opportunities to run dressed up as Santa!

Almost 300 Santas gathered in Luton's Wardown Park for its first Santa Run on Sunday 14th December 2008, which raised around £15,000. First to complete the run was 17 year-old Josh Noblett, who completed the 5km in just over 17 minutes. After collecting the first medal, Josh said:

> "It's been such a good, festive event and it's all for a great, local cause. The marshalls have been so supportive on the way round and I'm definitely going to take part again next year. I want to do it in a reindeer suit next time though!"

Also taking part on the day were some of the England Netball team, who came along with their local Superleague Netball club – the Mavericks. The team brought a Sky Sports television crew along to film them at the fun run, which was then aired before their match on Christmas Day that year. Naida Hutchinson, from the National Senior England squad, said:

> "We've all had fun today – it was a Personal Best for me! It is very different from our training and towards the end we were all feeling it! But it's for a good cause and we've had a great laugh dressing up in the Santa suits."

In a similar vein to the Midnight Walks, the charity built on the initial success of that first year in Luton and introduced Santa Runs in Stevenage and Bedford. In 2010, these raised £35,000 and in total the famous red suit and beard have been donned some 1,600 times during the Keech Santa Runs.

Going the

Scenes from the Midnight Walks, 2008- 2010, (including Billy Byrne from DIY SOS with walkers in 2009)

fra mile

The Santa Runs, 2008-2010

The Mavericks Netball Squad

Jacky Levinson and members of the 2007 hospice marathon team

Whilst the fun runs and walks naturally attract the large numbers, the lengths that some individuals go to for the charity are often quite extraordinary. Supporters of Keech have done firewalks (walking over 20ft of hot coals burning at 1200°F); they've climbed, walked, cycled and rowed over long distances; and they've taken on marathons, overseas treks and skydives!

For the London Marathon, held in April each year, there are usually around 20 – 30 runners in the hospice's official running team, including its five Gold Bond places.

Taking part in the 2007 marathon for the hospice was Jacky Levinson. Having stumbled over a pothole and run alongside running trees, a giant nurse and a pantomime Dame at various points in the course, Jacky explained how she felt on completing her second marathon:

> *"By the time I turned the corner towards the finish line I was really tired but wouldn't have been anywhere else in the world. As a participant in the London Marathon you are truly made to feel like a star for the day and to finish is the best feeling in the world. I knocked more than 16 minutes off last year's time and to top it all I have raised in excess of £2,000 for the Pasque, so I am very pleased."*

To date, London Marathon runners have raised £260,154 for Keech and along the way there have been some truly inspirational stories of personal achievement. Having survived a plane crash in 2007 that left him with 3rd degree burns to 60% of his body, partial paralysis in his feet and a life of countless surgical procedures, Jamie Hull decided to take part in the 2011 marathon. Walking the entire 26.2 miles, Jamie said:

> *"I was 32 when my accident happened. Before that I was very active and then suddenly I realised what it means to be vulnerable. Being in hospital so much, I met people with all kinds of injuries and illnesses, some of which were terminal. These were people who were going through a process a bit like me, but whereas my body is healing and repairing itself theirs won't. I think it was this realisation that made me want to do something for a local charity like*

Keech Hospice Care. It was an absolutely epic day and very inspiring. The buzz at the start of the marathon was incredible, where I was jammed in like cattle amongst 36,000 other runners. But as the day wore on gradually and more people finished, the atmosphere became a lot calmer. I basically gave it my best shot throughout the route and power walked my way straight through. The sheer volume of spectators lining the barriers was amazing, and they helped to spur us on throughout the day; cheering us and waving colourful flags and banners to motivate us all the way.

"It was slightly surreal when I finished at around 6pm, as the tranquil scene at the finish line was in complete contrast to when I started. The marathon was a double success for me: Despite my own injuries from the plane crash, I managed to cross the finish-line in 7 hrs 57 minutes flat, which was 3 minutes under my 8 hour personal target; and as a result of all my hard work fundraising for Keech Hospice Care, I'd gathered over £2,800 in sponsorship."

Taking on and achieving personal targets has been a theme for many in their fundraising efforts for Keech throughout the 'noughties'. Here's a few of their stories:

In 2003, Jeff Wood of St Albans cycled from Lands End to John O'Groats raising almost £3,000 for the children's hospice.

Gary Salvage of Luton raised over £500 by climbing Mount Everest in 2005 and then completing the Three Peaks Challenge (climbing Scafell Pike, Ben Nevis and Snowdon) in 24 hours in 2006.

> **"As a participant in the London Marathon you are truly made to feel like a star for the day and to finish is the best feeling in the world."**

2006

In 2006, four Hertfordshire men Chris Hemminway, Mark Stewart, Alan Inglis and Michael Bates headed straight for the most extreme climatic conditions on the planet as they trekked for 100 miles across the Polar ice cap for ten days. They raised an incredible £150,000 for the children's hospice.

The North Pole trek in 2006

2007

Kayaking 60 miles on the Grand Union Canal to London, Nick Kell from Milton Keynes, raised over £1,200 in 2007.

In 2007 Norman Owens, Robin Radford and friends walked 204 miles from Luton to Cromer along the Icknield Way and North Norfolk coastal path to raise £13,000. The money was used to fund a 'Concert Spectacular' held the following year and featuring the internationally acclaimed Morriston Orpheus Choir. A sell-out, the concert took the total raised to £23,000.

Jill Adam from St Albans was one of the adventurers who took on an overseas trek in 2007. Heading out on a 10 day trek along the Great Wall of China (walking, climbing and traversing over the ancient ruins), Jill raised approximately £3000.

2010

In 2010, 19 fearless fundraisers headed to India for a ten day trip which raised £60,000 for the hospices. The group took on a volunteering project at the Cancer Hospice in Delhi before embarking on a trek through the mountainous Himachal Pradesh area of Northern India.

The trekkers up a mountain in India, 2010

The archives at Keech house thousands of similar stories, each charting the completion of an amazing feat and individual triumph over hills, mountains, rivers and plains. However, there is another group of people who've gone that extra mile by taking to the skies.

A character from the US sitcom, The Big Bang Theory, was quoted in one episode as saying:

"A fear of heights is illogical. A fear of falling, on the other hand, is prudent and evolutionary"

Facing both fears, since 2004, over 550 people have taken part in skydives – jumping from a plane travelling at 10,000ft and freefalling at speeds of up to 130mph! Such is the popularity of the idea of jumping from a plane for the hospice that the company which runs the events, Skyline, says Keech is the charity that has sent the highest number of people along to take part. Those who have joined in with this exhilarating experience include many members of staff, family members of those who have received care at one of the hospices and members of the general public. It's also an event which has attracted people from across a very broad age range.

In 2006, Michael Coward, from Luton defied his name when he undertook the skydive as part of his 75th birthday celebrations. Having heard about it while attending one of the charity's Chinese Banquet evenings, Michael raised almost £900 in donations mainly received from friends at the Luton Probus Club. Speaking after his jump, Michael said:

"Cloud had gathered when it was my turn to jump and to fall through them was an amazing experience. I was scheduled on the same jump as a mother whose child uses the children's hospice. To raise money for Keech Cottage was fantastic, but to meet families who it directly supports made it all the more worthwhile."

Over five decades younger, but with the same level of motivation, was a 22 year-old student with Cerebral Palsy, Mohammed Shahzad Hossain, also known as 'Shaz', from Watford. Shaz, who raised over £450 when he took to the skies in 2007, said:

"I had a friend that used to go to Keech and I visited the hospice and heard a lot about how Keech supports families who are in that situation. It has always been one of my life goals to do a skydive and as I have Cerebral Palsy, it is my opinion that nobody should be limited from doing anything that they want to do and that you should live life to the full. The whole experience was really amazing. When you are sitting on the edge of the plane looking down at the clouds and are about to jump, you know it is too late to be scared. Once you're out and in the sky, it is literally breathtaking. I absolutely recommend anyone to take part in the next one, with or without a disability."

With the question of what it is about Keech that makes so many people want to go jump out of a plane (even some who have quite visibly been terrified), lingering in the air, the answers are varied and plentiful – they do it for the thrill, they do it to tick off an ambition and they do it because of a connection they feel with the hospices. Regardless of their reason, this is a group which have collectively raised in excess of £200,000 over the years and that's a fundraising feat of some stature.

"To raise money for Keech Cottage was fantastic, but to meet families who it directly supports made it all the more worthwhile."

205

All the fun of the fair

Whilst some relish in the thrills and spills of fundraising for Keech, the gruelling marathons or dare-devil leaps of faith are not for everyone. Some prefer to get involved through the slightly more static local community events such as shows, festivals, fêtes, carnivals and barn dances. While these may not raise the adrenaline levels quite so much, over the years they certainly have raised the income for Keech.

One of the earliest of such events began as a garden fête, held in the field opposite the original adult hospice for the first time in 1991. Volunteering with the hospice from the day it opened, John Adams recollects how he got involved in what grew into a large local event that many will remember.

> "I was asked by Roger Sharp, who was the official part-time fundraiser, if I could help – or my family and neighbours could help. My task was to organise a coconut shy and I was able to get some cups to hold the coconuts and some netting to run the coconut shy, but that clearly wasn't adequate. We needed more equipment than that, so we raided the nearby farmyards and obtained some corrugated sheets of iron and some timber and made up a proper coconut shy and it took a fair bit of money on the day."

The fête was held in the hospice gardens again the following year but the logistics of getting cars in and out of the lane were by that time becoming something of a problem. In 1993, the fête was held in the walled garden area of Stockwood Park and then in 1994 it moved again to Luton Hoo. Unfortunately, with non-stop torrential rain and many seeing the venue as too far out of town, the event that year proved non-profitable. From thereon the fête moved to Barnfield College's New Bedford Road site in Luton and took on the new name of the Midsummer Show – a flagship event for the hospice. With more room at Barnfield, this gave scope for a wider range of activities. There were more stalls, fun fair rides, exhibitions such as dog shows and gymnastic displays and a barbecue. Held on a Sunday, the event was also combined with a 5-a-side football tournament which was part of a programme of sports activities run in the school holidays for children by Luton Town Youth Development.

With so much more to do, visitors to the show tended to stay longer and within the ten years it ran at Barnfield, the occasion grew from a one day show to a full weekend of events. Before it came to an end in 2005, the Midsummer weekend included a popular fish and chip supper and dance, held on the Friday night in one of the marquees; a separate event on the Saturday such as antique valuation days, magic shows and more; and then the Midsummer Show itself on the Sunday. As John Adams remembers, co-ordinating it took a lot of hard work:

> "As a guideline, we were probably generating somewhere between £15,000-£18,000 profit every year, which was a good sum of money, but it took a lot of work to do it."

Having raised a total of £248,525 over the years, although the Midsummer Show had always been successful, as time went on, the scale of the event and local authority legislation meant that the charity would have to employ professionals to handle the site security and health and safety matters and the cost of doing that became prohibitive. The work of the Fundraising Committee, however, went on and in the years that followed they organised barn dances (generating around £5,000-£6,000 per year), dances in schools, quiz nights and murder/mystery nights.

"Another popular event..."

Fun times for all at the Midsummer Shows

Crafts for
Christmas at
Barnfield College

Another popular local event for the charity was Crafts for Christmas which began in 1998. Prior to this, the charity had been running a Christmas bazaar in local school halls, but then Barnfield College agreed that the charity could use the venue over the weekend of the autumn half-term for its new two-day Crafts for Christmas event. For a few years, the charity kept both events going but as the bigger Crafts for Christmas took off, the Christmas Bazaar was phased out.

Still running today, Crafts for Christmas attracts some of the leading local craftspeople as stallholders and has raised almost £80,000 for the charity. Many local people go every year and see it as their opportunity to browse for gifts while also getting their hospice calendar, diaries and annual draw tickets purchased. For Keech it marks the beginning of the countdown to Christmas itself!

As well as the events organised by the charity's fundraising team and committee, Keech has participated in many of the large scale local events over the years.

The hospice has had a float or stall at every Luton Carnival since 1996 and won several prizes for its creatively themed floats along the way. Other than animal charities, Keech was one of the first charities to be given permission to go along to the Herts County Show held at Redbourn Show Ground in 2003 and has been taking part ever since. Today, Keech also regularly has a presence at the Bedford River festival, Bedford Kite festival, Dunstable Carnival, Houghton Regis Carnival and the Harpenden Highland Gathering. Whilst these may not be major money-makers, the charity does not underestimate the value of showing the face of the hospice in terms of public recognition. Fundraising Director, Jacqui Shepherd, explains further:

"Every time we join one of these events we have a wonderful team of volunteers to help and we use it as an opportunity to spread the word. We have collections but the real worth is in the footfall. There are literally thousands of people going along to these events and we do our best to talk to as many as possible about the work of the hospices and the ways they can support us. Potentially that can lead to all kinds of revenue in the future."

Tea, bananas and a bit of small change

Whilst the big events and challenges continue to raise substantial funds for Keech Hospice Care, in many ways these are the fundraisers which follow the trends and can suffer from participant apathy after a few years. As such they often have a limited lifespan and only continue to be successful when they change with the times. However, there are some timeless things that people do to raise money for Keech. For a great many years, local people have been holding tea parties, dressing up in silly costumes, filling collection boxes, purchasing Christmas Bell badges, putting stickers in their cars and much more. Taking collection boxes alone, the charity has issued these to over 3,000 sites in the community since 1990. Over the years, these have raised just under £500,000 for Keech – not bad for a collection of small change!

Originated through the umbrella charity, Help the Hospices, the 'Tea at Three' campaign offered supporters another very simple way to raise funds – by inviting friends or colleagues around for a cuppa (and maybe a cake or a biscuit too). As one of the many people who hosted an event at their house for several years in a row, Pauline Bradley commented:

"We have tea, cakes and sandwiches, sell home grown plants and handmade birthday cards and also hold a raffle. My guests help on the day and often bring something along for the raffle. I buy a few things too so we get a good range of prizes like bottles of wine or house plants.

"For my family, friends and myself, Tea at Three is an event we all enjoy and look forward to. It's great to get together with everyone who supports the hospice and quite often people come that I haven't seen for a while, so it's also a lovely way to catch up with old friends."

In June 2008, the Friends of Keech group working in Luton and South Bedfordshire went a step further by hosting a large public Tea at Three event in Barton Village Hall. As well as tea and refreshments, the group organised a variety of stalls selling books, plants, cakes, fresh produce, crafts, games and a barbecue for those feeling peckish.

The hospice itself has hosted many a Tea at Three, usually in its day care area, bringing patients and staff together. In 2011, to coincide with the marriage of Prince William and Kate Middleton, the hospice hosted a Royal Tea at Three. In total the simple act of raising a cuppa has raised just under £75,000 for Keech.

No story of fundraising could be told without a mention of all the wonderful and often wacky costumes people have adorned for the hospices. There have been members of staff dressed as sunflowers and superheroes; volunteers heading out as clowns and even trustees have got in on the act. One memorable moment came in 1999 when Trustee, Jack Sapsworth dressed up as a banana and proceeded to go along to his Rotary Club. All in the name of charity, of course.

"In total the simple act of raising a cuppa has raised just under £75,000 for Keech."

Dressing up for Keech

Fame at last

Although they haven't quite gone as far as dressing up for Keech, over its history, there have been many celebrities who have given the charity their support. From the early days when Bob Monkhouse turned up to officially mark out the site of the original adult hospice, a host of celebrities have since visited the adult or children's hospice and given their support, which in turn has helped raise awareness and income. Here's a taste of what some have done:

2000

In **2000**, BBC Three Counties Radio presenter, Jon Gaunt held a weekend telethon where listeners were encouraged to raise funds and give up their time to build a multi-sensory garden in the grounds of the children's hospice. With raised flower beds, a water feature and a huge wind chime, the garden has been enjoyed by hundreds of families over the years and, to this day it is still known as 'Gaunty's Garden.'

Cliff Parisi, 'Minty' from EastEnders, helped Keech to get involved in two celebrity cricket matches involving other members of the EastEnders cast in **2005**.

2008

In September **2008**, Joe Swash (aka Mickey in EastEnders) started the charity's first Midnight Walk in Luton with a New Year's style countdown to Midnight, chatting and posing for photographs with many of the ladies on the night.

England and Saracens rugby star, Andy Farrell and his wife Colleen have supported the charity over a number of years and, for instance, donated a selection of money-can't-buy prizes for auction one year at the charity's Butterfly Ball.

Celebrity chef, Jean-Christophe Novelli, came on board in **2009** and since then has donated cookery classes as auction prizes; conducted cooking with chocolate sessions at the children's hospice; created a unique Keech recipe calendar in **2010**; and took part in ITV's All Star Mr and Mrs show with his wife to raise £10,000 for Keech.

Weather presenter, Sian Lloyd was quoted as saying the charity "captured her heart" when she became the face of the charity's 2009 Tea at Three campaign.

2010

After visiting the hospice, Billy Byrne from DIY SOS decided to join the charity's team of adventurers who set off on a trek across India in 2010.

Keen to help his local community, England cricketer, Monty Panesar, fronted a collection box campaign for Keech called 'Gimme 5' in 2009 encouraging people to save their 5p pieces which has raised £10,000 so far.

W ell known author and BBC Songs of Praise presenter, Pam Rhodes, has long been a dedicated supporter of the charity. As well as writing many a word and undertaking public speaking roles on behalf of Keech, Pam also fronted the charity's 'Walk of Life' campaign which helped to raise funds for the building of the new adult In-patient Unit. Individuals, local companies and community groups paid to dedicate a paving stone within the special path which Pam officially opened for the charity in June 2009. At that time almost 300 stones had been dedicated, raising £57,000 for the adult hospice.

Pam Rhodes

T elevision presenter and the face of BBC's Formula 1, Jake Humphrey, first visited the hospice in 2009 and immediately pledged to spread the message about the charity's work. When Keech decided to lay a second pathway with dedications for the children's hospice, Jake was one of the first to buy a brick and fronted the publicity campaign. Having been involved with the hospice ever since, Jake is now an official Ambassador for the charity. Commenting on his commitment to Keech, Jake said:

Jake Humphrey opening the Stepping Stones path in 2009

"I expected to find my first visit to the hospice rather difficult and sad. However, it was quite the opposite and that was the single biggest aspect for getting involved. I found the visit incredibly positive, uplifting and rewarding, and remarkably happy. Considering what happens at the hospice, it is a testament to the staff and the support the hospice receives that it is a great and positive place to be.

"I've helped with a few events including asking my F1 colleagues, David Coulthard and Eddie Jordan, to make a butterfly picture to be auctioned for the charity. I also fronted the 'Stepping Stones' appeal and had a wonderful day launching the path and getting my friends and family to buy some bricks. To see parents who have lost children there actually wanting to return and do what they can for the future of Keech is an example of the impact that the hospice has on people's lives and I'm so proud I was involved in helping raise awareness and funds.

"The standout memory of my time at the hospice until now has been the strength of both staff and the parents of ill children. I will never forget meeting the young parents of a very ill child who sadly didn't have long left. The parents were given the time and space to make the most of their final days together and the staff knew just how to support them - when to give them space, when they needed company and how to help them understand their situation and their feelings. I was so impressed by both the parents and the staff and will never forget the atmosphere of love and support that day. I just want places like Keech to be celebrating birthdays for many years to come, for people to realise the work they are doing on people's doorstep and how reliant they are on local funds, support and donations to keep doing the work they do."

The
final
word

Whilst the hospice celebrates its 21st anniversary, fundraising for the hospice probably has more of a 25 year history. In that time, many of the ways in which supporters get involved in fundraising have changed while others remain very similar to what they were all those years ago.

Probably the biggest trends in fundraising for Keech today are the growth of corporate support (see chapter 12) and the increased interest in mass participation events such as the Midnight Walks and Santa Runs.

However, what runs throughout all the fundraising efforts for Keech, past and present, is the fact that out in its local community, there are a countless number of people willing to get out and do their bit. Added to that is the unyielding efforts of Keech's fundraising teams over the years.

In joining Keech, these are people who have taken on a job that goes far beyond the 9-5. In fact they can be seen out and about across the whole community – in school assemblies, at Rotary lunches, giving presentations about Keech to local community groups and even promoting the Santa Runs by standing outside a football ground dressed as Santa at the weekend!

Whether it's by running a marathon or a market stall, jumping from a plane or stepping into a silly costume, Keech Hospice Care couldn't be without its local community and the support it provides year after year.

A fundraising *phenomenom*
Carole's story

An act of mindless vandalism back in 1998 brought the charity one of its most prolific voluntary fundraisers, someone who is still volunteering today and is on the way to helping Keech raise a magnificent £200,000! While the children's hospice was still being built, sadly vandals turned up to the site one night and smashed all the windows which were due to be fitted over the next few days. Carole Young remembers hearing the story come out on the local radio:

"I was in between jobs at the time, taking some time out and so often listened to local radio. Keech was mentioned quite a lot but I'd never really paid much attention until I heard about these vandals that had smashed the windows. It was upsetting to hear such a thing and so I thought I'd see if I could do something to help. It was nearing Christmas time and I was involved in a New Years Eve function, so I asked everybody if we could do a raffle and think about the hospice. At the time, even though I was really happy to help, I remember being nervous about bringing the money we raised up to the hospice. I don't know why but I guess that, like a lot of people, I found the word 'hospice' a bit daunting. I actually waited for about three weeks before going along that first time! A year later, I did the same thing and, that time, when I came up with the money, I met a lovely lady who thanked me and asked if I'd like to help at the hospice. I gave it some thought and then came up again for a chat with someone in the fundraising team and before I knew it, there I was helping out once a week with some administration work."

Since then, Carole's involvement with the hospice has escalated and over the years she has passed on the word and, in some way or another introduced most of her friends to the hospice (some of whom have ended up as trustees). She has opened her house once a year for Tea at Three events; visited a great many community groups to give talks about the hospice; helped at innumerable fundraising events run by the charity and organised her own local events such as fish and chip suppers/ dances.

On top of that, Carole still supports the current fundraising team with some voluntary administration work once a week and has even turned up at the hospice with her husband on Christmas Day to help the care team – doing the washing, ironing, making tea – whatever has been needed!

In 2001, Carole and her friend, Judith Kelsey took on a small table at Ampthill's weekly market and asked friends and neighbours for anything they could sell to raise funds for the hospice. In their first year, they raised two or three thousand pounds and, as each year that figure has increased, so too has the size of their market stall! Today they have a very large stall with two other friends, Sue Pitkin and Pauline Maguire, helping out. Rain or shine, the four ladies pitch up every Thursday to sell goods they collect from their neighbourhood and store at their own homes. Together they are approaching a landmark total of £200,000 raised for the hospice. Carole said:

"The people we know are so good; they're constantly putting things aside for us. Be it a standing lamp or a bar of soap, toys, books or games, we'll literally take anything that we can fit in the car and that we think we can sell. And we've had everything, from ironing boards to keyboards to guitars. You name it, we've sold it! Sadly Judith passed away this year and so has not seen her name in this book, but I know she will always be remembered very fondly by everyone at the market. However, we were really pleased that, before she died, we were able to tell her that in 2011 we raised £15,000 - our best ever year!"

After the countless hours Carole has spent ringing round for support, standing in the rain at events, stuffing envelopes in the fundraising office and standing up in front of community groups to talk about Keech, Carole now says she has a huge emotional attachment to Keech:

"By helping with fundraising I've come across so many wonderful people – there have been some real characters and I've always got a story to tell.

"I remember one lady in a church where I did a talk who firstly told me off for sitting in her seat and then said I needed to learn how to speak properly because she couldn't hear a word!

"I could never have done any of this without that support."

Carole Young (left) with Maria Barry, Director of Income in 2008

"Then there was a lady who turned up at the market one day and asked if she could have some Light up a Life pins to give to everybody at the funeral of her husband. He had been ill in hospital and had actually been excited when he was told he would be going to the hospice. Sadly he passed away before that happened, but the lady said she felt that he died happy because, in his mind, he was going to the hospice. Keech clearly meant a lot to her and I just thought that was quite a magical story. Even more recently, I went to pick up a cheque from a group who had been fundraising. I didn't know much about them but when I got there, it turned out to be some lovely young men who all had Down's Syndrome. They had raised money by doing up a garden for somebody and there was a cheque for us. While I was thanking them and telling them about Keech, they were clapping me and I said, 'no, you've done this, I'm going to be the one clapping you!' It was amazing. So, whether they bring smiles, frowns, laughter or tears, these are stories you just wouldn't get anywhere else and they always stick with you. It's hugely rewarding."

In 2008, Carole received a surprise phone call from local newspaper, The Herald and Post, to say she had been nominated in the Charity Fundraiser of the year category of their Pride in Luton awards. Carole went on to win the award and was given a plaque to mark the achievement. Carole said:

"Of course it was a proud moment but I just wanted to go out and share it with everyone! So many people have been involved in helping to raise money for Keech and I could never have done any of this without that support. For me, the biggest reward is that feeling you get every time you come up the drive to the hospice. You can't help but feel you are coming to a very special place. That's why I'm there each week and, while I can, that's what I'll be doing with the rest of my life.

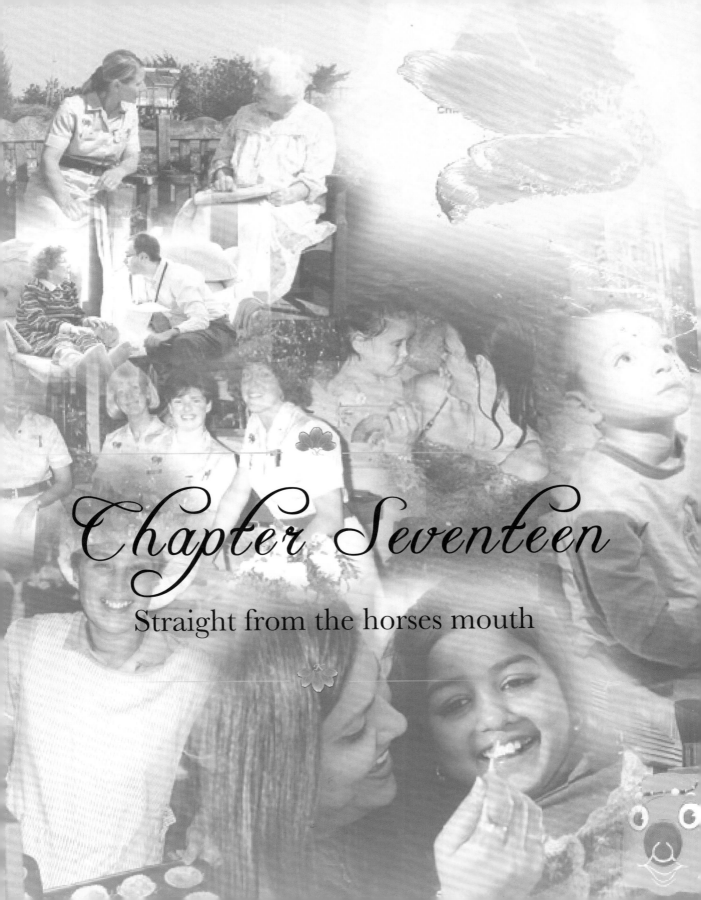

Chapter Seventeen

Straight from the horses mouth

From just a handful of people in the beginning, Keech Hospice Care today has some 200 members of staff and around 1000 volunteers! Over its 21 year lifespan, the myriad of people that have been involved in the charity's work are incalculable, but facts and figures alone do not tell the true story.

on't For get Your Trai ners! ♥ Keech

♥ Keech
Hospice Care

The real story of the charity comes from the many tales that staff and volunteers who have worked there over the years have to tell. Here's where we turn this book over to some of those people to hear their stories.

....

In a society where people have largely moved away from the idea of a job-for-life, it is no surprise that most of the people who were involved with the hospice at the very beginning have now moved on. But, there are always the exceptions (or should we say the exceptional?), one of which is Liz Bradley who joined the hospice as Catering Manager on day one and is still there today. Holding the accolade as the longest serving member of staff, Liz still vividly remembers her job interview:

"I first heard about the job in the local paper and I thought 'I will give it a whirl'. I came up for the interview in the afternoon and there was about six to eight people, including Barbara Kettley, Zena Skinner and Jackie Tritton interviewing me. I remember it was really scary and so daunting, but it went well. I'd barely got home before the phone was ringing to offer me the job."

Liz was given the responsibility of setting up the kitchens, planning the catering service and recruiting a new team. With just a few weeks to go before the kitchen needed to be ready to serve food to staff and volunteers, she says there was no time to waste.

"I started work and was told 'There's your kitchen – sort it'! I had to get all the suppliers and go shopping. Zena Skinner was absolutely amazing and helped to introduce me to suppliers like Roland Allen. We have still got the stainless steel saucepans I bought 21 years ago!"

Starting as a team of two staff plus volunteers, cooking for around 20 people at the most, the catering team today has grown into a team of ten staff plus volunteers who, at times, can be cooking for up to 80 people a day.

During her years at the charity, Liz has faced the many hurdles that comes with adapting to a growing organisation – everything from working out how to cater across two hospices after the opening of the children's unit to managing the additional demands that came with catering for the external conferences and functions which were held above the children's hospice for many years. However, it is the unchanged personal approach to catering for hospice patients which Liz is most proud of. She commented:

"A hospice must treat each patient as an individual. If you have got somebody who is not happy to eat something because it is too heavy or hard, then you simply give them something else. From the start, we had to change the way that we cooked to make the food easier for the patients to eat. For example, we often found that patients couldn't eat a grilled lamb or pork chop – it was too hard. So we just changed it and braised the meats instead. We were changing all the time, but always with the patients' needs in mind. What we've always aimed to do is give our patients the flexibility of having what they want – for breakfast, lunch and supper."

With the size of the charity so much bigger today than when she first started, Liz's work has shifted from the kitchen towards a more administrative role – managing the team, budgeting, planning and training – but she still keeps a hand in with the cooking as often as she can. Looking back, Liz remembers many landmarks, including serving a cup of tea to HRH the Countess of Wessex during the official fifth birthday celebrations of Keech Cottage in 2005. But, above all, one very special outing tops Liz's list of highlights:

"My best memory was going to see the Queen a couple of years ago. Apparently, Mike Keel, had put me forward for the draw and my name got pulled out. So, along with one of the nurses, Mike and several other people from the hospice, I went along to St James' Palace to see the Queen. We went for afternoon tea and had cocktails and wine in the Palace. It was just superb."

The Noller family, from Luton, have another rather extraordinary tale to tell. Between them they have volunteered at the hospice since it very first started. The first to get involved, Shirley Noller, initially helped with fundraising for the building of the adult hospice but when that was completed, began volunteering on the In-patient Unit. Shirley said:

Princess Anne with Zena Skinner and Liz Bradley (right) at the Royal opening of Keech Cottage in 2000

"I remember hearing about the hospice plan on local Three Counties Radio and felt it was a wonderful idea to have a hospice built locally. They were appealing for fundraising support so I thought I must do something to help. I did things like hold coffee mornings and lunches at home to raise money, but then decided I'd like to be involved at the hospice itself. In March 1992, I started volunteering on the adult unit one evening a month but after I retired in 1998 I changed my hours to a half day, every week. I am not a qualified nurse, but I help where I can: collecting the patients' menus, helping with washing patients, answering the telephone, serving lunches and so on. The hospice acts as a great reassurance to people and I've always loved being a part of that."

Shirley's daughter, Claire, joined the fundraising volunteers in 1993 and has regularly helped with events and awareness stands. Adrian Noller joined his wife and daughter as a volunteer in 1997, whilst continuing to carry out his job at Luton Airport. He began as a collector of fortnightly lottery payments and continued this on retirement in 1999 when he extended his role to volunteer driver. Being involved for so many years, Shirley notes the many changes her family have seen:

"In the early days, the hospice was very 'cosy'. Staff and volunteer numbers were very small and you knew nearly everyone. I found it very happy and friendly. People wanted the hospice to be a success. Everyone was very proud of it. Over the years the hospice has grown and changed into a major business helping a huge number of people. I think the charity has handled the business element well, without losing any of the personal care they provide to patients."

Reflecting on her time at the hospice, Claire summarised the family's commitment with a sentiment to which they all agree:

"We all enjoy helping such an important local charity. The hospice is so special to all of us and I can't ever imagine a time when it's not part of our lives."

At work: kitchen and dining area at the hospice

Liz, right, dressed up for the Queen's garden party

The Noller family

Personal *Connections*

> "The hospice is so special to all of us and I can't ever imagine a time when it's not part of our lives."

Keech Hospice Care is a place, which has, over the years, touched the lives of so many local people, supporting them through the illness or death of a friend or relative. Almost inevitably, quite a number of the people who end up working or volunteering at Keech have had some personal experience of that support and been attracted to the role due to the connection they feel with the hospice. For some, that personal connection was made long before the hospice even opened. This was the case for Kathy Scott whose husband, Harry, was diagnosed with cancer in 1986. While the hospice was still just a germ of an idea in Dr Wink White's mind, Barbara Kettley was working in the community as a MacMillan nurse and supported the Scott family at home. Kathy said:

Touching lives: many volunteers and staff members feel inspired to work here due to personal connections

"Barbara came out to talk to Harry and the girls and me and she was an absolute angel. Then, when the hospice was completed and Barbara was made Matron, I wrote to her to say how pleased I was. She wrote back to me and I just couldn't believe it because she remembered everything about the girls and I thought 'That's a gift'."

Shortly afterwards, the charity was actively recruiting volunteers and Kathy signed up to help on reception on a Saturday morning. She also got involved in visiting people at home as part of the bereavement support group, helped at the summer fêtes and organised her own events to raise funds. She added:

When people talked about the hospice in those days they were very nervous. It was nice for me to be able to tell them how different their ideas were to what was actually happening. I met some lovely people – they were very kind and would come in, chuck their money down and be gone. You would try to call them back to get their name and number and they would say it is not important. But it was important to us. In all I saw and all I met, it was something Barbara Kettley did which sticks in my mind. It was the anniversary of Harry's death and I remember I'd taken the girls to school, got home and hadn't even taken my coat off when there was a knock at the door. When I opened it Barbara was standing there with a bunch of flowers. I can't say how much that meant to me."

Staff members, Pat Whiting, Lisa Sellers and Jackie Mann, are among the many who have been inspired to work at Keech Hospice Care because of the care and compassion they have seen given to close relatives. Pat Whiting, who now works in fundraising, remembers her first contact with the charity:

"In May 2009, my husband was an in-patient at the hospice for three weeks. During his stay, on a Sunday, it was my birthday. John told the staff and the nurses organised a lunch for the both of us. It was a beautiful day. They set up a table in the courtyard for us, complete with umbrella, and served us a very nice lunch. This for me is a very happy memory from a very difficult time."

For Lisa Sellers, it was the way her grandmother was cared for at the hospice in 2002 which led to her own career choice of nursing in the field of palliative care. She said:

"When my Nana was diagnosed with cancer of the pancreas she became very poorly quickly and palliative care was the only option, which she struggled to accept.

"She went into the hospice for symptom control and was allocated 'Iris' room for her stay. Her name was Iris too! While there she was very comfortable and treated very well by the nurses and doctors. She also seemed to find peace and became more accepting of her illness. When I visited, I was pleased to see how warm and friendly the hospice was. It didn't seem to be a sad place. I was a student nurse at the time and I realised this was where I would like to work. I aspired to be like the nurses I had met."

Lisa was a student nurse at the time and, after qualifying, she spent a number of years at the Luton & Dunstable Hospital before applying for a job as a Staff Nurse at Keech. Eight years after her grandmother had stayed at the hospice, Lisa was surprised but not fazed to find herself being interviewed in the 'Iris' room:

"I knew my Nana was sending me good luck and I felt her around me. I felt confident I'd got the job! I am so happy that I am now doing that job which I love. As a nurse on the adult unit we experience so much with our patients and their families and I am so proud to say I work at Keech. I sometimes feel I should pay them for having me! Thank you Nana."

Once again, it was the idea of working somewhere which had been of so much help to her family which saw Jackie Mann navigate towards Keech Hospice Care. Back in 1994, Jackie's husband, Harry, was suffering with a brain tumour and a MacMillan nurse introduced them to Keech. She remembers:

"We were both fairly young and had a toddler so it was a difficult time for the family. Initially, Harry went to the Day Centre once a week and thoroughly enjoyed these visits, especially the massage sessions that helped ease his pain. He was a very proud family man so didn't burden me with thoughts about his illness. I believe the Day Centre gave him the opportunity to discuss this, so that we could have happy family times at home. Harry also used the In-patient Unit on a couple of occasions when we both needed a rest and it allowed me to concentrate on our son."

Jump ahead to 2009 and, while looking for a change of career, Jackie stumbled upon the role of Retail Administrator at Keech, applied and got the job. She said:

"I am so pleased I joined the team as it is a very rewarding job that is growing as we rapidly expand the retail outlets. I work with a great team and feel privileged to be able to fundraise so that future people can enjoy the benefit that my family were given in our hour of need."

A Privileged *Opportunity*

Ask anyone who has worked at Keech Hospice Care about their time there and you'll invoke a wide range of emotional responses – some recall a sense of achievement alongside the concern they experienced throughout the more difficult times; others remember a place filled with a mix of tears, laughter, compassion and courage. But, whatever memories they hold, the most common turn of phrase to be heard is of the wonderful opportunity they have had and the 'privilege' they feel to have been part of the Keech story. This was certainly true for Marian Townsend and Ruth Hammond who became part of the original nursing team for the Luton and South Bedfordshire Hospice back in 1991.

"I aspired to be like the nurses I had met."

"Some
Recall...
a sense of achievement alongside the concern they experienced throughout the more difficult times; others remember a place filled with a mix of tears, laughter, compassion and courage."

As nurses and mothers of young children, Ruth and Marion were inspired to work for the adult hospice but found a sticking point in the need to work full shifts. Undeterred they decided to apply as a full-time job share, something which would allow them to share shifts and childcare. Marion remembers:

"Our applications were combined and sent in a bulging envelope explaining what we were proposing – We think this perhaps got us noticed! Our idea of the job share was innovative at the time and seemed to be well received by the panel... and we got the job."

Marion and Ruth were left to plan who worked which shifts and who looked after the six children they had between them. Ruth added:

"I'm still not sure which one of us got the short straw but this worked really well for us and for the hospice that got two brains (sometimes) for the price of one! We began our hospice life as naive new recruits, passionate to develop our knowledge and expertise in palliative care. We embraced all aspects of the hospice life and saw many changes while we were there. We eventually dissolved the job share as our children grew and became senior members of the nursing team. In time we both moved on to pastures new as Community Macmillan Nurses but we will always be grateful for the opportunity the hospice gave us to work as the first job share and to be members of the original nursing team. We feel privileged and proud to remember these roots."

Another former member of staff, Jo McDonnell looks back at her time as Nurse Manager at the children's hospice with the same sense of contentment. She said:

"I spent eleven amazing years working at Keech Hospice Care and have some wonderful memories that will stay with me. There were some challenging times – like spending my first month there squashed with around 30 other staff into the room known as the 'chapel' because the building wasn't finished. But there were plenty of fun times too – like taking part in the Luton Carnival with children and their families over the years. With typical English tradition we did it all weathers, from very cold and very wet to beautiful sunshine. However, in all my time at Keech, the most precious memories that I take with me are those of the children and the families and how I have been privileged to be part of their lives, no matter how long or short."

Someone else who remembers her time at the charity as challenging but rewarding is Joan Gray. Back in 1995, Joan began working at Keech through a secondment opportunity provided by her employers, Marks and Spencer. Initially working one day a week with Roger Sharp in an office above the charity's Dunstable shop, Joan's secondment lasted a year. After this she applied for a full-time job at the hospice to organise the volunteering function and helping General Manager, Martin Johnson, with the charity's administration. Over the years that followed, Joan's role grew and during her time at the charity she helped to set up new systems for managing volunteers; was integral to setting in place new standards, policies and procedures for all aspects of the charity's work; took on site management of all the hospice buildings; oversaw improvements to the hospice kitchens; and oversaw an ambitious expansion plan for the charity's chain of retail shops. By the time she left her role as Director of Business and Administration in 2008, the charity was a significantly changed organisation. Joan recalls:

"When I came for my secondment I think there were two people in finance, three administrators, one fundraiser and an assistant. We were in an office above the Dunstable shop and moved up to the hospice once the day hospice extension had been completed. At the hospice, I could see that the care of the patients was great and everyone's hearts were in the right place but, coming from a commercial background, I found the atmosphere a bit too relaxed. I saw the hospice grow from a small operation which kind of made up the rules as it went along to something very professional, with standards in place where they needed to be and with much more of a visionary direction. To see the charity get to that stage was very rewarding."

From Director to Housekeeper, Doctor to Receptionist, the rewards for those who have worked at Keech seem to stick in the mind. For some it's been watching the charity evolve from small beginnings; for others it's been the amazing people they've met along the way; and for others it's simply that feeling of doing something useful and having left a mark. Pat Frost (or Little Pat as she is known) says it's the latter which caught and kept her loyalty to the charity. Beginning as a volunteer helping with the laundry in 2003, Pat then became a bank housekeeper. She said:

"I was volunteering and then one week the housekeepers were very short on staff so they asked if I'd give them a helping hand. Before you could blink, there I was in uniform as a bank housekeeper, having passed my test with a trolley! We are a very diverse group of ladies. We can go from cleaning toilets to moving furniture, to flower arranging, to washing and ironing, to digging the garden. We are a happy bunch and always laughing. I'd like to think I've left a bit of a mark at Keech, even if it is only within all the curtains that are hanging around the building."

"I could see that the care of patients was great and everyone's hearts were in the right place."

Jo McDonnell

Jobsharing staff nurses, Ruth (left) and Marian (right) in 1991

Little Pat, centre, with her hospice colleagues

Naughty but nice!

The hospice movement has from very early days, had to address the double misconception that a hospice is somewhere people only go to die and consequently must be terribly gloomy. At Keech Hospice Care, of course there are sad days, but people who walk through the doors of either hospice soon find there is lots of fun, laughter and a little bit of mischief too.

If ever there was a way to dispel the misconception that a children's hospice must be a sad place to work, the current care team seem to have found it in their tales! Among them is current Children's Service Manager, Jeanette Farrow's story from one of her very first days at Keech:

"One of the children's mums came out of the bedroom one day and handed me a full nappy! Being new, I firstly had to work out what I was supposed to do with it and once I had achieved that and disposed of the offending item, staff then informed me I had to go through the nappy and study the contents!
How mean was that."

Then there are the endless accounts of mischief that some of the cheekiest young residents have got into at the hospice. Shift Leader, Emily Hayes remembers getting a night shift shock:

"I hadn't been at Keech very long and 'D' was in for a stay and he was very mobile at the time. It was the early hours of the morning, we had checked on the kids and they were all asleep (or so we thought). A short while later I was in the treatment room, when I heard footsteps coming up the corridor. Thinking it was a colleague, I stayed where I was and got the shock of my life when I turned around and saw 'D' stood before me, the Little Monkey!"

Music Therapist, Kathryn Barker gave another example of how, working with the children at Keech has brought her much laughter:

"I was working with Matthew and his mum, Carolyn, at home. It was coming towards the end of our session and Matthew appeared to have fallen asleep with his head and shoulders against the harp whilst I was playing.

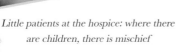

Little patients at the hospice: where there are children, there is mischief

> "There are sad days, but people who walk through the doors of either hospice soon find there is lots of *Fun,* laughter and a little bit of mischief too."

> *"I wondered how I was going to pack away without waking him and as I stopped, he opened his eyes and looked straight at me, reaching out with his hand to play the strings. We laughed and I carried on playing as he seemed to drift off again. The next time I stopped he gave a huge sigh and reached out again as if to say 'I didn't tell you you could stop playing!'. Carolyn and I spent the next few minutes laughing and talking about the amount of 'attitude' her son had."*

But it's not only the youngest of the Keech community which have been responsible for the 'naughtier' moments. Before the children's service had been established, Dr Elizabeth Horak recalls one Christmas Day when the relative of a patient gave her a special bottle of "Chateauneuf du Pape". Describing the day as one of the nicest Christmas Days of her life, Dr Horak said:

> *"As it was a very special, expensive present, I hesitated for a moment whether it was appropriate to accept, then quickly decided. 'Could this be part of a special Christmas occasion?' I asked the generous visitor. He was not sure what I meant, but generously agreed. Thus, the nurses helped to collect 44 glasses (the head-count in the building), found some tit-bits, cut up a Christmas pudding, and all the patients, relatives, nurses, children, the receptionist and the doctor gathered in the hall. The patients who were bed-bound were taken there in their bed.*

> *"When all were there, we had a feast and shared the wine. What started as an impromptu idea of dealing with a slightly embarrassing, too nice a present, became a symbolic memory for me. Naturally, if you calculate, 44 portions of 75 ml of wine means we all had about 1/3 of a teaspoon... but, it was one of the nicest wines I ever tasted, and what an effect it had! We all felt warm, relaxed and suddenly started to behave like a large family.*

> *"It was natural to see the patients, at the last Christmas in their life sharing a sip of wine with their grandchildren. While I am not sure that the kids liked the taste of wine, I am convinced that they perceived the symbolic meaning of sharing something special. They understood that it was a special wine, a special occasion, and they were part of it. "*

It's a volunteer's *World*

The 1,000 strong team of volunteers that Keech benefits from today come from all walks of life and help the charity with every aspect of its work – fundraising, retail, gardening, housekeeping, manning reception, driving patients and much more. Judging by the awards the charity gives out each year for 5, 10, 15 and now 20 years of voluntary service, it seems that those who come to Keech to volunteer tend to stick around for a long time. Janet Ellis, who has helped the charity with reception duties for 20 years, remembers the pegging out ceremony:

"It was a dull grey day with rain threatening and a small crowd had gathered at the top of Great Bramingham Lane. Suddenly a very sun-tanned and smiling Bob Monkhouse arrived with his lovely wife to begin the ceremony of putting in the first post. After a short speech and much applause, Bob placed the post in position and this began the building of what

Volunteering at the hospice reception

was to be called the Luton and South Bedfordshire Hospice. Little did I know at the time that the hospice would grow from its small beginning and that I would undertake the duties of a volunteer receptionist for 20 years!"

Carole Spalding started as a Hospice at Home volunteer 21 years ago and has seen it grow from a very small but dedicated unit in the beginning to a much bigger service which merged with Keech in 2010. Carole says it is the people she has met over the years which have kept things interesting:

"I remember one of my clients would insist on sitting outside in the garden, come rain or shine. I think just sitting in the garden boosted his spirits. There was another lady who I took shopping every week and she would insist on making me a cappuccino when we got home. You can have too much of a good thing but I enjoyed taking her shopping and got quite close to her. I still miss our little shopping sprees."

Ken Grunwell put his name down as a volunteer early in 1991, before the adult hospice had opened. He began helping as a day care driver and doing craft activities with patients in the Day Care Unit. In 1991, Ken's wife, Margaret, got involved and together they manned a stall at a fundraising bazaar. After this, the couple organised 'Bring and Buy' events at their home and in 1994, Margaret also began volunteering in the first hospice shop in Luton's Arndale Centre. Today, Ken continues to help by training up minibus drivers and Margaret still works in the charity's central Luton shop, which relocated to Park Street in September 2009. Ken said:

"Over the last 20 years, Margaret and I have been involved with various fundraising events and volunteer activities, an experience that has been very enjoyable and rewarding. The feedback we have had from patients over the years has all been good which makes our efforts worthwhile. We hope to continue in the future."

A volunteer arranges flowers at the hospice

Having also given 20 years, helping to arrange flowers at the hospice, Vera Day is another volunteer who feels she has gained much from her time at Keech:

"I have always said, life for me began at 60 and helping to arrange the hospice flowers over the last twenty years has been most enjoyable and certainly enhanced my life. I have seen many changes and met numerous and lovely volunteers who work with such good humour. It has been a pleasure to be involved with the wonderful work that is done by all. Long may my visits to the hospice continue."

One of the
Oldest residents
at Keech

Not every resident at Keech can tell their own story. In fact, one of the oldest residents at the hospice today fits this category - a Bird of Paradise plant donated in 2011. Occupying a sunny corner at Keech, the magnificent plant (Latin name Strelitzia Regina) was kindly given to the hospice by Luton resident, Tony Gittins in memory of his wife, Helen who died at the hospice in 2006, aged 53.

The plant, which was grown from seed by its original owner around 1930, was nurtured by Helen and Tony in their conservatory for nearly 40 years. As well as providing a wonderful memorial for Helen, the plant is special for a number of reasons. At 80 years old, it is older than its counterpart at Kew Gardens and is also one of the very few Bird of Paradise plants to have double headed flowers which bloom on more than 20 occasions between September and March every year.

Since making the donation, Tony has advised the housekeeping team at Keech about how to best look after the plant and still comes in to the hospice to prune it occasionally. He said:

> *"During her life, Helen was someone who gave a lot to others. She was always doing something to help out a cause or charity she believed in but, when she wasn't doing that, she'd be in the conservatory looking after the plants – the Bird of Paradise was her particular pride and joy. Sadly she was taken from us at an unjust age and died in the care of the hospice. After that I wanted the plant to continue to give happiness to others and Keech seemed the only fitting place for it to rest."*

A younger bird of paradise plant was donated by a hospice maintenance volunteer. The housekeeping team today have affectionately given the two plants their own personal names. Housekeeper, Pat Frost commented further:

> *"We have two new members of our team, Oscar and Son of Oscar. Oscar is the name I gave them to feel more at home. We have had some lovely blooms from big Oscar. Baby Oscar is still thinking about it."*

Chapter Eighteen

Top cats

"The story of Keech hospice Care would not be complete without the memories of those who have led the charity through its tumultuous lifespan."

'Lights of Love' in 2000: an event that was first introduced by David Ashton

In many minds, the top cats at the hospice were (and always will be) Meggie and Alfie, the kittens who became residents in 1991 and remained at the hospice for all of their nine lives. They were such a part of the hospice's life that Chapter 20 of this book has been dedicated purely to them!

However...

However, there have of course been some 'second in commands' and the story of Keech Hospice Care would not be complete without the memories of those who have led the charity through its tumultuous lifespan.

The charity's day-to-day life was initially led by a voluntary Bursar, John Britton, however the first General Manager of the charity was David Ashton. Known for his integrity and genial nature, David oversaw the very early development of the adult hospice service and introduced the idea of a 'Lights of Love' event. Now called 'Light up a Life' the event has been run every year since 1994, bringing thousands of local people together to remember and celebrate the memory of a loved one. Sadly, David died before seeing how the care provided at the hospice would grow or how the Lights of Love event would take shape. Working alongside him in those early days was Zena Skinner, who gave this tribute to the man she knew:

> *"David was a wonderful man. What I loved about him was that every morning the first thing he did was to go round and say 'good morning' to everybody and make sure they were all right. People used to say 'Have you seen David?' and they'd say 'oh yes, he came round and had a joke with us'. Of course there wasn't as many staff back then but he made time for everybody and, in such an early stage of an organisation, I felt that was very important."*

Local poet, Audrey Tingey (nee Strudwick), wrote and bestowed poetry books to the hospice to help with early fundraising. In the charity's 21st year she kindly agreed to write a piece in David's memory:

Remembering
David Ashton

A man of such integrity,
Respected by us all.
We'd take our problems to him,
However large or small.

He'd do his best to solve them, he
Would help us organise
The running of the hospice, and
Was really very wise.

He introduced the 'Lights of Love',
Which flourish to this day.
He never saw their great success,
He sadly passed away.

But some of us remember still
And often times recall,
That every day he found the time
To speak to one and all.

And so we go on and on
With memories galore,
But think it's time to finish off
With just one memory more.

He worked for us so tirelessly,
Why there was nothing spared,
But most of all we're grateful for
The way he always cared.

While the charity grieved the loss of its leader, it also needed someone new to take on the overall responsibility of running and developing the hospice service. Martin Johnson took up that role for six years, between April 1994 and July 2000. Having worked for 21 years in the Air Force, followed by six years in financial services, Martin remembers how he came to join the hospice:

"After the financial crash of 1987 I had taken on the challenge of helping companies sort out their financial problems and stop them from going bust. But by the beginning of 1994 that was grinding to a halt and that's when I realised that, at the age of 14, I'd had the idea of joining the Air Force with a view to going on to work in the charity world. That's when I saw the advert for the role at the hospice. I met the trustees, lead by Wink White, and I can remember saying to them something along the lines of 'well if you want to change and develop, that's what I'll do', the implication being that that if they didn't want that, don't bother to employ me!"

The trustees did appoint Martin and from the word go his mandate for change took off. During his six years as General Manager, Martin oversaw the £500,000 investment and opening of the adult Day Hospice within what was then called the Marjorie Steele Wing; the planning, fundraising and building of the £3 million Keech Cottage Children's Hospice project; and some major work in developing and improving the hospice's clinical reputation as a specialist palliative care service through improved medical cover, a not so minor challenge that Martin felt was achieved with the support of Dr Elizabeth Horak. Summarising his time at the charity and the atmosphere at the hospice during his time, Martin commented:

"It was a time of change and rapid expansion. After the Day Hospice building had been completed we moved on to look at medical cover. Then immediately after that came the entire children's hospice project. For that we built up a team and got the fundraising and building completed in record time.

"The challenge of such growth is of course to retain the good things about what had been in place before and for me it was very important to retain the warmth and supportive atmosphere witnessed every day of my time at the charity.

"I think probably the most difficult time for me came when we started taking in our first child patients. I was engaging with some of these kids and found it very emotional to know these children were not going to grow up. I always had great admiration and respect for the staff who were so dedicated to these children but, as a father of four, I kept being forced to reflect on how I would feel in such circumstances."

By 2000, not long after the opening of Keech Cottage Children's Hospice, Martin came to the decision to move on, taking up a new position as Chief Executive of The Thalidomide Trust. He said:

"In a relatively short space of time I felt we had reformed and expanded the adult hospice care services and made specialist children's hospice services available to our community. I could see that the developments I had been brought in to do had come to an end."

That new leader was to be John Quill. Chief Executive at the charity from December 2000 until September 2007, John had in fact started his working life as an accountant, was ordained as a Church of England priest and worked in two parishes and then became Social Responsibility Officer in Worcester Diocese. John had also worked for Watford Council and as Chief Executive of another charity before coming to Keech. Arriving at Keech at a time when it was becoming clear that the charity was in financial crisis, John had to find a way to go public with a deficit of £1 million, a legacy of the children's hospice building costs outweighing the funds raised. His focus then was to rebuild relationships with local healthcare commissioners, raise the level of the charity's fundraising efforts and boost confidence among the public.

Challenges along the way: Martin Johnson quoted in the local newspaper over the vandalism at the Keech Cottage building site in September 1999

Martin Johnson, left, with Chairman John Maddox in 2000

Sick! Vandals wreck work on hospice

During his time at Keech, John oversaw many challenges, from the transformation of an inherited 'hole in the ground' into the state of the art hydrotherapy pool by 2002, to planning and fundraising for a new adult In-patient Unit in his last year at the charity. In between, John was involved in the growth of support and therapy services and a diversification of income streams through an expanded fundraising team. He also took a hands-on approach in supporting some of the charity's major events such as the Midsummer Show and Lights of Love. Commenting on one of his significant challenges, building bridges with health and other statutory authorities, John comments:

> *"Statutory funding for hospices is, I think, an issue which will never go away. I spent countless hours negotiating with commissioners from Bedfordshire and Hertfordshire, trying to persuade them that, among all the other priorities they had, palliative care should be high up on the list. That was never an easy task but I was pleased with the good relationships we managed to create during that time."*

John Quill (below) appealing to the public about the hospice's cash crisis

The decisions John had to make during his time were not always orthodox or popular, for instance the changes made at the children's hospice to stop offering pre-booked respite/holiday care that were chronicled back in chapter 15. But, whilst John remembers this and the many other challenges he faced as the tough and demanding part of his job, he also recalls that not every day was a serious one! Amidst all the work to improve the charity's finances and develop its care, John remembers one particularly funny moment. Each year, the charity holds volunteer evenings where the Chief Executive makes a presentation about that year's developments and provides opportunities for questions. As well as doing this, John decided the occasion was also worthy of something a little more light-hearted and, perhaps calling upon his previous experience in the clergy, broke out into a song. Accompanied by, Graeme, the music therapist, on the piano and the Bereavement Care Manager and fellow vocalist, Jeff Lewcock, they took a traditional song (Supercalifragilisticexpialidocious) and reinvented it with lyrics about volunteers and the things that were going on at the hospice. Here's a snippet:

John: You know, you can say it backwards, which is "docious-ali-expi-listic-fragi-cali-repus", but that's going a bit too far, don't you think?

Jeff: Indubitably. And what would volunteers be backwards?

John: Mmm that'll be teers-nu-lov

Jeff: That sounds about right.

Describing the effect of everyone witnessing the Chief Executive singing, John said:

"It was a bit of fun and I think it helped people to see me as approachable. What I didn't realise was that, after that first time, word got around and by the time the volunteer evenings came around again the next year, a song was expected!"

After seven years of leading (and singing for) Keech, in September 2007 John decided it was time to move on. Leaving the charity in much improved financial health, John began his new life as a volunteer assistant priest within his local parish and as a part-time self-employed management consultant. Before saying a final farewell to Keech, he said:

"I'm proud today (as I always have been) of the dedication I see from staff and volunteers; the consistent support we receive from our community; the good relationships we have established with healthcare commissioners; and the fact that I'll be able to hand on the CE role knowing the charity is in good shape. Most of all I'm proud to have been a part of an organisation that makes such a difference to the lives of so many people."

Following John's departure, David White took up the post of Chief Executive for the next three years. David had been the Chief Executive of an adult hospice before and had also been involved in the Hospice Movement through consultancy work he had done for organisations such as Help the Hospices and so came with a good understanding of hospices. The children's hospice was new to him but he soon picked up what it involved and needed.

David inherited the building of a new adult In-patient Unit and saw this through to completion. Also during his tenure, the two hospices were unified under the new branding of 'Keech Hospice Care' and the charity achieved external accreditation and recognition by being awarded the status of Accredited Hospice from the Hospice Accreditation Quality Unit.

David also spotted the untapped potential of the retail operation. His insight transformed the operation and, by very astute recruiting and leadership, the profit from the shops increased to nearly £1m per year. The charity is hopeful that its birthday year of 2012 will see it crowned as the country's second most profitable hospice retail operation – an amazing achievement from last place a few years ago! Mike Keel recalls:

"David was a completely different Chief Executive to work for than his predecessor. His experience and knowledge of the hospice world that he had built up over the years and through his consultancy work was inspiring and fascinating. I learnt an enormous amount during his short time with us".

David White (left)
and Mike Keel
(right) in 2011

However, these were also years which saw a global banking crisis and recession and, with rising costs coupled with everyone keeping a tighter reign on their wallets, Keech Hospice Care did not escape the impact. Regrettably, by 2009, the charity made the decision to use some of its valuable reserves to ensure services kept going and everyone at the charity rallied round and searched for areas to make savings without cutting any vital services to patients. Although the charity had not plunged into full flung crisis, many who were working or volunteering at the hospice remember it as an unsettling time.

David left the charity in 2010 and, after a period of working as Chief Executive in an 'acting' capacity, Mike Keel, the then Deputy Chief Executive, was appointed as the new (and current) Chief Executive in April 2011. Mike first came to Keech as Nursing Manager back in 1996 and soon became the 'right hand man' for successive Chief Executives; guiding and advising them about clinical and service developments. His clinical background and hospice expertise made him the perfect choice for trustees looking for someone who could boost morale, strengthen the charity's position and 'steady the boat'. Taking up the role in somewhat challenging circumstances, Mike commented:

"Times are difficult at the moment, not just for charities but for everyone. I therefore see it as my main responsibility to ensure we can keep providing our vital services to those who need them and that we can find the money we need to do this by being ever more imaginative and innovative in our fundraising. Most importantly, the people who do support us need to know that we will use every penny wisely and effectively. At the same time, I am dedicated to ensuring we never lose track of what our founders knew to be the embodiment of good hospice care – a high-quality service with a strong community focus."

True to his word, in the short space of time that Mike has led the charity, he has strengthened the board of trustees with new members and put in place a new hospice-wide strategy, focused on providing quality care for more people while making sure the organisation is well run and remains financially secure. One physical example of this already being put into practice can be seen in the improvements made to adult day care that were completed in 2011. While the project had been on a 'wish-list' for some time, care was taken to ensure refurbishments only went ahead when the project had been fully funded and that patients' needs were placed at the heart of the plans. The project clearly reflected the central pledge of the charity's new strategy:

As long as people continue to have unmet palliative care needs, Keech Hospice Care will strive to develop its services and partnerships to address those needs.

What the future holds for any charity can be uncertain, but over the next few pages of this book, Mike Keel explains how this pledge will be taken forward; leading the way for the next chapter in the life of Keech Hospice Care.

I am *dedicated* to ensuring we never lose track of what our founders knew to be the embodiment of good hospice care - a high quality service with a strong community focus."

Chapter Nineteen

Keech Hospice Care in the next 21 years

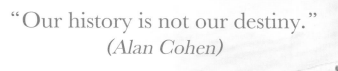

"Our history is not our destiny."
(Alan Cohen)

Vehicles
and contents
are left at
owners own risk

"I don't think the founders
could have imagined the Keech
Hospice Care we have today
when they were setting it up."

Over the following pages, the hospice's current
Chief Executive, Mike Keel, shares his thoughts
on the charity's possible challenges in the future.

Compiling this book has given us the opportunity to look at the charity's history as a whole. It's not until you see it like this that you realise how much is has progressed and changed. I don't think the founders could have imagined the Keech Hospice Care we have today when they were setting it up. The world is changing so fast and so much that it would be futile for me to attempt to try it for the next 21 years. What I can do is describe the influences (or levers in modern day parlance!) that will affect the charity and what it does over the next few years and the course they may set us on.

The future of palliative *Care*

Keech Hospice Care is part of seismic changes in health and social care in the United Kingdom. Not since the creation of the National Health Service (NHS) in 1948 has such significant changes been proposed to our welfare systems.Improvements in health care and people's general well-being since the war has meant we live longer than before but those extra years aren't necessarily healthy ones. Average life expectancy has soared to 80 years old, eight years higher than in the 1970s, and is predicted to increase another 10 years over the next 25. The number of people over the age of 85 is expected to increase by two and half times in the next 25 years. Another important contributor to this is the decline in deaths from cardiovascular disease. However, with the increase in obesity, there is widespread concern that this increase in life expectancy in Europe and other high-income countries may come to an end. The charity must be ready to adapt to this demographic shift and ageing population.

In the children's service we have already seen younger and younger babies needing palliative care as more of them survive birth with a life-limiting illness. Similarly, at the other end of childhood, advances in medical care means more children are surviving longer with their illness and succumb in early adulthood where before they died in childhood. The adult hospice will need to start taking more of these young people into its care. In future, more people will be living and dying with complex health and social care needs, many of which require palliative care expertise. Of one thing we can be sure: the demand for palliative care at the end of life is going to increase. Presently, family members provide the majority of informal care to the elderly but with changing demographics, this will alter. At the moment few elderly people are divorced; childless; or widowed and most are married. The cohort born in the mid-1950s show a different pattern and this may put more strain on the care services with less family around to provide care.

Dignity in death and proper end of life care are important issues for most people. This requires a holistic approach to care that transcends health and social care boundaries and is fully integrated; something which the government has acknowledged is the best approach for all care.

This is not only health and social care integration but also state, private and voluntary integration in a variety of settings (hospital, community and home). This will mean that palliative care will need to be provided in many different ways and not just from purpose-built standalone hospice buildings – the service will more resemble 'palliative care consultancy teams' supporting GPs, District Nurses, carers, hospitals, care homes, schools, etc. and will need to intervene at a much earlier stage of terminal illness to have better effect.

Adult Care Homes will take on more and more of the current hospice role and families with children diagnosed with a life-limiting condition will receive more of their care at home – even quite high-tech and specialist care. Hospices and other specialist palliative care providers will be expected to be more involved in the education of others so our expertise is available to all people who need it, wherever they are.

The charity will need to work more collaboratively with other organisations and sectors. Commissioners will be looking for organisations to come together to provide a comprehensive service. It is natural that the hospice should be the lead for palliative care, but we will need to draw in other partners like Macmillan, Marie Curie, nursing homes and hospitals and work together to ensure the patient and family receive the best care, wherever they need and want it. Keech has done some of this but a lot more needs to happen.

The future of hospice *funding*

The thorny issue of state funding of the hospice comes up frequently in the book and conversations with supporters and staff. The future of hospice funding is more difficult to predict. The state will not be able to fund the spiralling costs of health and social care as it stands now and there'll be greater dependency of people using their own resources (be it money or family/friends to help – the Big Society). What the state will fund will be quite discreet – we already know that the Funding Review carried out in 2009/10 has recognised that some parts of palliative care must continue to be funded from voluntary sources while the state picks up 'core' clinical interventions through a tariff system. The government wants to encourage wider use of 'personal budgets' and create more competition for all providers - be they state operated, private or voluntary. Keech will have to learn to operate in this new competitive environment.

What is known is that good funding of care in the community or at home has been shown to be much cheaper than expensive hospital stays (and hospice stays if they're paid at full cost). The charity may have an opportunity through the new funding system to attract more state funding for its core clinical work, but will always need the generous support of its community to fund the full service and develop its role in the new community-focussed services. Keech much adjust to the more austere reality we are facing.

The future of the *Charity*

There is concern that future generations may not have the same community spirit or where-with-all to support charities in the way our current band of strong supporters has over the last twenty one years. I'm not sure this is necessarily true. We see daily examples of young people engaging with the charity to help or support it. The resilient spirit of the past can be revived. Keech must ensure the community grasps the enormity and urgency of the situation if we are to continue to care for their loved ones and the government must continue to encourage volunteering and giving (especially through legacies) so that charities can continue to play their vital part in society. Our current mantra at the charity is that 'Free Care Costs'. Although it's free to the patients and families, someone has paid for it and this is usually the patient's community – their family, friends, neighbours, colleagues and other people they may not know or have ever met. This places a duty on all of us to secure the charity for today because somebody else will secure it for our future. I finish with the wise words of the founder of the modern day hospice in the UK, Dame Cicely Saunders:

You matter because you are you,
and you matter to the end of your life.
We will do all we can not only to help you die peacefully,
but also to live until you die.

"All of the nurses and carers were fantastic - we always felt they cared for Mum in a way that went above and beyond the call of duty as nothing was ever too much trouble."

Thank You Keech
for everything"

The Pollard family's story

While the role of hospices may change in future years, Keech Hospice Care today has pledged to do all it can to help anyone within its community with palliative care needs. With the continued and dedicated support of its community, Keech will continue to do this 24-hours a day, 365 days a year. As one final reminder of just how significant that care can be, Andrea Pollard tells the story of how her family spent one Christmas at Keech.

During Christmas 2007, Keech helped to care for my Mum, Marguerite at the hospice before she died in January. At the same time, the children's hospice at Keech helped my husband, Mark and I to care for our 3-year old daughter, Rebecca. Rebecca had a condition called Infantile Polyarteritis Nodosa (PAN) Vasculitis. The blood vessels in Rebecca's brain blocked and caused her to have a series of mini strokes. This left her with a very serious brain injury and meant Rebecca was on constant medication and required round the clock care. We had been receiving support from Keech for a while – at home and at the hospice and found that Keech truly changed our lives. Before Keech, Rebecca wouldn't go to anyone except my mum, and because of all her medical needs there was no-one else who knew how to look after her properly anyway. We felt isolated, but that all changed. Whenever Rebecca was at Keech, we knew she was properly cared for and was in very safe hands. While Rebecca was still a baby, in 2005, my Mum, Marguerite was diagnosed with cancer. She recovered after chemotherapy and radiotherapy treatment but became ill once more in 2007 when it was found she had bowel cancer. The cancer spread and her condition deteriorated quickly. On 12th December 2007 she was admitted to the adult hospice.

Andrea, Mark and Rebecca Pollard

"Whenever Rebecca was at Keech, we knew she was properly cared for and was in very safe hands."

Rebecca with Marguerite

At home she had been in a lot of pain, had great difficulty sleeping or eating and couldn't even properly take a bath. When she came into the hospice it was to get help with her symptoms but she felt awful. At that stage she had just given up. But with the help of everyone at the hospice, her symptoms got under control and within just a few days she had started to feel better. The bed she had there had a special pressure relieving mattress which finally helped her sleep more comfortably. She was also helped to enjoy a Jacuzzi bath, had music therapy and massage at her bedside and even got some of her appetite back. After a week or so she was back to her jovial, chirpy self and was saying if she could live like this for another six months she'd be happy! Being at the hospice made such a difference. All of the nurses and carers were fantastic – we always felt they cared for Mum in a way that went above and beyond the call of duty as nothing was ever too much trouble. And, because the children's hospice helped us to look after Rebecca, that meant I could spend the time I needed with Mum during her last days. When Mum died she couldn't have been in a better place and, although we had spent all this time at the hospices for sad reasons, everyone there had helped to make it into a much better time than we ever could have expected.

Thank you Keech for everything.

Andrea, Mum to Rebecca and daughter of Marguerite

Chapter Twenty

Meow

"The way the two cats gave their support to patients, relatives and the nursing team was something the staff at the hospice still marvel at."

Soon after the adult hospice opened in 1991, two little additions made an appearance – Alfie and Meggie, the hospice cats.

Coming to the hospice as kittens, the brother and sister duo were to become more than much-loved pets. Throughout their entire lives they were seen as part of the team.

Soon after the adult hospice opened in 1991, two little additions made an appearance – Alfie and Meggie, the hospice cats. Coming to the hospice as kittens, the brother and sister duo were to become more than much-loved pets. Throughout their entire lives they were seen as part of the team. Nurse, Pam Ciba, remembers meeting them when she first came to the charity back in 1997:

"I'd always been a cat lover so when I found out the hospice had cats I was over the moon. The two of them were quite different – there was Alfie, big and bold and then Meggie who was much more the little lady, but they were both full of character and very knowing. By the time I arrived, Alfie had gained a bit of a reputation for giving out the odd swipe if you got too close, but somehow he just took to me and I never even got a scratch!"

Alfie's reputation meant that a fair number of people got that 'odd swipe' and as a result his name appears in the hospice's accident book a few times! Nothing was ever very serious though and his scratches were unfortunately usually in retaliation to someone getting a little too close for comfort.

While Alfie was seen as the feisty one, often bringing back mice and voles from his night-time hunting trips, Meggie claimed the role of the serene lady. Staff remember her as being a bit of a secret antagonist though as, like many a brother and sister, she would start a fight but make sure Alfie was the one that got the blame! She knew how to rule the roost.

The way the two cats gave their support to patients, relatives and the nursing team was something the staff at the hospice still marvel at, as Pam recalls:

"Often when a patient was very poorly or something was about to happen, they would wander up and down the corridor on the unit, making that kind of crying sound that cats do. Meggie was especially knowing and often she'd go into a patient's room and just lie down with them. They would find it a real comfort. The strange thing was that both cats could read the unit. Most families adored them but there were of course people who didn't like cats and Alfie and Meggie seemed to sense that and knew when to stay away. Also, when a patient died and was leaving the hospice, Alfie was always there at the door."

Living at the hospice for nearly two decades, the cats were familiar faces to everyone. They'd get spoilt by the kitchen staff and were often seen outside the canteen hatch, crying for a titbit – especially on Fridays, fish day! There were times when one of them (usually Alfie) would sneak into someone's office and steal a sandwich from a desk. Then there were other times when one (usually Meggie) would disappear for a bit and eventually be found curled up asleep in a patient's locker. Luckily, throughout their lives, local veterinarian Julia Bowness, gave her services for free to take care of the health of both cats. When Alfie became poorly she even gave him acupuncture, all in her own time. Sadly, the cats used up their nine lives and Meggie died in March 2007, to be followed by Alfie in January 2010. Senior Sister, Shirley Gadsden says their memory lives on:

"Alfie and Meggie were such a benefit to everyone at the hospice. Patients and their families found their company soothing and relatives who come back to visit us still ask about them. We all loved being in a place where there were animals and all the nurses thought of them as part of the team. On a sad day they'd be there to give you a cuddle. They had their limits though and I remember many a time when things got a bit tough on the unit, Alfie would turn up in my office to get away from it all for a bit, just needing a bit of space the same way we do I suppose. I know everyone found them a real comfort and they're sorely missed."

Alfie and Meggie have been immortalised in many ways. Over the years they've had several mentions in local newspapers and have had their images taken in both photographs and paintings. They now also have their names engraved on a paving stone in the hospice's 'Walk of Life' pathway and the nursing team planted a Pussy Willow tree just in front of the hospice in their memory, a fitting tribute to two small but special members of the team.

"While *Alfie* was
seen as the feisty one...

Meggie
...claimed the role of
the serene lady."

Alfie and Meggie in their later years

Nurses from the unit planting the Pussy willow tree

The cats' paving stone in the Walk of Life

Our Hos

We had to have a hospice
The need was really great,
So many people suffering
Who really couldn't wait.

Thus, over twenty years ago
The seeds of it were sown,
And as the little acorns do
The mighty Oak has grown

pice

And now it's twenty one years old
We watch it grow with pride,
The hospice like the acorn grows
The door is open wide

So now we have to carry on
Continuing to strive,
The spirit of those early years
We'll always keep alive.

Audrey Tingey

Index